Transitions
Ingham

(Rob Frears)

D1645174

PUBLICATIONS
OF THE
JOINT INFORMATION SERVICE

Halfway Houses for the Mentally Ill: A Study of Programs and Problems, by Raymond M. Glasscote, M.A., Jon E. Gudeman, M.D., and J. Richard Elpers, M.D. 1971.

Salary Ranges of Personnel Employed in State Mental Hospitals and Community Mental Health Centers — 1970. 1970.

The Staff of the Mental Health Center: A Field Study, by Raymond M. Glasscote, M.A., and Jon E. Gudeman, M.D. 1969.

The Community Mental Health Center: An Interim Appraisal, by Raymond M. Glasscote, M.A., James N. Sussex, M.D., Elaine Cumming, Ph.D., and Lauren H. Smith, M.D. 1969.

Partial Hospitalization for the Mentally Ill: A Study of Programs and Problems, by Raymond M. Glasscote, M.A., Alan M. Kraft, M.D., Sidney M. Glassman, Ph.D., and William W. Jepson, M.D. 1969.

The Mentally Ill Offender: A Survey of Treatment Programs, by Patricia L. Scheidemandel and Charles K. Kanno. 1969.

Legal Services and Community Mental Health Centers, by Henry Weihofen, J.S.D. 1969.

Health Insurance for Mental Illness, by Patricia L. Scheidemandel, Charles K. Kanno, and Raymond M. Glasscote. 1968.

The Treatment of Alcoholism: A Study of Programs and Problems, by Raymond M. Glasscote, M.A., Thomas F. A. Plaut, Ph.D., Donald W. Hammersley, M.D., Francis J. O'Neill, M.D., Morris E. Chafetz, M.D., and Elaine Cumming, Ph.D. 1967.

Approaches to the Care of Long-Term Mental Patients, by Helen Padula, M.S.W., Raymond M. Glasscote, M.A., and Elaine Cumming, Ph.D. 1968.

The Psychiatric Emergency: A Study of Patterns of Service, by Raymond M. Glasscote, M.A., Elaine Cumming, Ph.D., Donald W. Hammersley, M.D., Lucy D. Ozarin, M.D., and Lauren H. Smith, M.D. 1966.

General Hospital Psychiatric Units: A National Survey, by Raymond M. Glasscote and Charles K. Kanno. 1965.

Private Psychiatric Hospitals: A National Survey, by Charles K. Kanno and Raymond M. Glasscote. 1966.

The Community Mental Health Center: An Analysis of Existing Models, by Raymond M. Glasscote, M.A., David Sanders, M.D., M.P.H., H. M. Forstenzer, M.S., and A. R. Foley, M.D. 1964.

REHABILITATING THE MENTALLY ILL IN THE COMMUNITY

A Study of
Psychosocial Rehabilitation Centers

REHABILITATING THE MENTALLY ILL IN THE COMMUNITY

A Study of Psychosocial Rehabilitation Centers

RAYMOND M. GLASSCOTE, M.A.
Chief, Joint Information Service

ELAINE CUMMING, Ph.D.
Director, Mental Health Research Unit,
New York State Department of
Mental Hygiene

IRVIN D. RUTMAN, Ph.D.
Executive Director,
Horizon House, Philadelphia

JAMES N. SUSSEX, M.D.
Chairman, Department of Psychiatry,
University of Miami School of Medicine

SIDNEY M. GLASSMAN, Ph.D.
Chief of Psychology,
Fort Logan Mental Health Center

Foreword by
WALTER E. BARTON, M.D.
Medical Director,
American Psychiatric Association

A publication of
THE JOINT INFORMATION SERVICE
of the
AMERICAN PSYCHIATRIC ASSOCIATION
and the
NATIONAL ASSOCIATION FOR MENTAL HEALTH

WASHINGTON, D.C., 1971

THE JOINT INFORMATION SERVICE
of the AMERICAN PSYCHIATRIC ASSOCIATION
and the NATIONAL ASSOCIATION FOR MENTAL HEALTH

EXECUTIVE COMMITTEE

DONALD W. HAMMERSLEY, M.D., serves as permanent professional consultant to the Joint Information Service.

The Joint Information Service is administratively attached to the APA Division of Public Affairs, which is headed by ROBERT L. ROBINSON.

Additional copies of this publication are available from THE JOINT INFORMATION SERVICE, 1700 18th Street, N.W., Washington, D.C. 20009, at $6.00, with discount for quantity purchases.

The study reported herein was carried out under a cost-sharing contract between the National Institute of Mental Health and the Joint Information Service. Approximately three quarters of the funds for the project were furnished under Public Health Service Contract No. PH-43-67-1322.

FOREWORD

WALTER E. BARTON, M.D., *Medical Director*
American Psychiatric Association

From the earliest recorded history, man has labored to meet his subsistence needs. As for the mentally ill, Pinel wrote, almost two centuries ago, "Moderate employment and regular exercise, cooperating with the energies of nature herself, restored him [the patient], in a short time, to the full enjoyment of his intellectual faculties."

Benjamin Rush, James Connolly, Esquirol, and Samuel Woodward were among those who stated their conviction that work facilitated recovery from mental illness.

Hermann Simon of Germany left an indelible mark upon European psychiatry. He employed work, as re-education, to establish what he believed were good health habits. He reported that 98 percent of his patients worked. The factory-type paid employment for patients, common in Europe, is the heritage of Simon's approach.

In our society, social status is largely determined by occupational achievement. Mental patients who succeeded in remaining out of the hospital, according to Freeman and Simmons, demonstrated a positive correlation between adequate work performance and high-level adjustment. Their study also showed that success in remaining out of the hospital and fulfilling the family's expectations was related to the patient's ability to find work and to contribute to his own support and that of his family.

When medical treatment of a disease or an injury has accomplished all that it can, the individual may still have a handicap. Rehabilitation is the process by which the handicapped person is helped to function in a manner that is more satisfying to himself and increases his usefulness in society.

Wing says that the definition of medical rehabilitation should have three parts: *a*) a statement of aim, ideally to resettle an individual in his normal domestic setting and at work appropriate to his talents; *b*) a description of the long-term difficulties which hinder the achievement of this aim, the handicaps, whether they be physiological or psychologcial dysfunctions, the social stresses, and the lack of self-confidence, or the difficulty in finding work because of prejudice; *c*) the methods necessary to minimize the handicaps or compensate for them.

Mental hospitals have long been concerned with the process of rehabilitation. In *Impressions of European Psychiatry* I have described the factory-type work carried out in mental hospitals in Europe, such as building wood and metal furniture and custom-made equipment, assembling and packaging toys, manufacturing electrical assemblies and extension cords, making boxes and repairing crates, filling perfume bottles, and preparing tulip bulbs for shipment.

The English, who studied the Dutch system and its sheltered workshops, incorporated job retraining not only into the mental hospitals but also into the industrial rehabilitation units in various parts of the country. This action facilitated the return to useful work.

In the Soviet Union, the Neuropsychiatric Dispensary has extensive facilities for daytime employment in a sheltered shop. The government determines what useful articles will be made for sale. The patient retains part of the proceeds as his compensation.

Community mental health services in this country have not developed their rehabilitation program or sheltered shops or factory-type work activities to any great extent as of the present time. Experimentation is to be encouraged with the development of job skills and social skills that will assist in overcoming the residual handicaps of mental illness that remain.

The authors of this Joint Information Service study have performed an important and useful service in calling attention to prototypes of rehabilitation centers now in operation in this country.

Washington, D.C.
December 1970

ACKNOWLEDGMENTS

The Joint Information Service is deeply grateful to the directors and staff members of the psychosocial rehabilitation centers which were the subject of this study. Six of the programs invested a great deal of time and effort in developing materials for us and in arranging for the field visits. We also express our appreciation to the directors of five other programs, who took the time to come to Washington and meet with us concerning issues and problems of developing and operating rehabilitation programs for the mentally ill. Dr. Walter Barton, Dr. Lucy Ozarin, Mr. Robert L. Robinson, Mr. Brian O'Connell, Dr. Herbert Butler, and Dr. Arthur Stein read the manuscript and made a number of useful suggestions. Particularly, we appreciate the support and assistance that we received throughout the study from Mr. Gary Palsgrove, Administrative Officer for the NIMH Division of Mental Health Service Programs, who served as project officer for the study.

CONTENTS

I. Introduction

FROM THE PERSPECTIVE of 1970, the past half century can be seen as a time in which service to the mentally ill was progressively moving from isolated and segregated institutions back into the community; if the process is far from complete, the trend and the accomplishments are unmistakable. The mentally ill had, of course, in earlier times been contained in the community—most often in jails and paupers homes. The movement to remove them from the community, even if in retrospect it does not seem to have worked out as well as was hoped, was humanitarian in origin and purpose. State hospitals were created in large numbers in the nineteenth century to provide an alternative to the jails and poorhouses. Unfortunately, within a few decades construction at state hospitals was sharply curtailed, and many of the existing facilities became overcrowded and dilapidated.

Perhaps the earliest deliberate move to provide treatment in the community for the seriously mentally ill can be viewed as the "psychopathic hospitals." These facilities, developed in most cases as components of medical training centers, provided a limited amount of inpatient treatment to individuals usually selected in order to provide a representative variety of pathology for teaching purposes, but they also developed research departments and outpatient treatment units. Thus, they represented an important new outreach of psychiatry towards the community. The first was established in 1906 at the University of Michigan. The second was established in 1912 as a special component within Boston State Hospital; later it became independent, and it operates today as the Massachusetts Mental Health Center. In ensuing years a number of additional psychopathic institutes were developed in other states. But because they were small facilities by design, they could provide service only to a limited number of people.

A closely related development which has since come to have a major influence on the locus of treatment for the mentally ill was the development of psychiatric units in general hospitals. By 1924, when the Henry Ford Hospital in Detroit established the first general hospital psychiatric section (in the modern sense), most state hospitals had become too

1

crowded and were too understaffed to provide a good quality of cus-tody—which was at the time their perceived purpose. Gradually a pioneering hospital here and there added such a section, but growth was slow, and by 1940 there were no more than about forty; their activities consisted in large part of "receiving" patients, who were then, in many cases, channeled on to state hospitals. But some of the general hospital units provided a humane, appropriately supervised setting in which the "reception" function could be carried out.

An intercurrent development was the creation of the outpatient mental hygiene clinics. The first of these dates prior to the twentieth century, but this type of facility, too, was slow in catching on. Some were established in the 1920's, followed by a period of great growth in the 1930's. Origi-nally conceived of as serving children, under the conviction that early intervention would prevent more serious and prolonged emotional dis-turbance in adulthood, the clinics gradually broadened to include the adult population as well.

The American involvement in World War II provided an important experience to psychiatry. It was often impossible to evacuate the man who had broken under the stress of battle; but it was observed that those psychiatric casualties treated immediately and right behind the front lines fared better than those who were evacuated. Largely as a result of this experience, agitation for additional general hospital psychiatric units intensified in the late 1940's. A concurrent development also had its effect. Electroshock therapy, developed in the late 1930's, had by the mid-1940's gained wide acceptance. An increasing number of privately practicing psychiatrists wanted the safeguards of a hospital setting within which to administer this new therapy. Thus, the number of general hos-pital psychiatric units increased rapidly from 1947 onward.

The 1950's brought the most important single development. After experimental use in the early years of that decade, a new category of medication was introduced into the state hospitals. The *antipsychotics,* or "major" tranquilizers, eliminated delusional and hallucinatory behav-ior in the majority of patients and reduced anxiety without impairing the ability to think and perceive. This new therapeutic agent had a great and immediate effect on state hospitals, as described later.

Propitiously timed, the Joint Commission on Mental Illness and Health came into being in 1955, at the behest of the American Psychi-atric Association. Chartered by Congress, it surveyed the inadequacies and fragmentation of the existing treatment resources, particularly the state hospitals, with their shortages of personnel, overcrowded and out-dated facilities, and waiting lists. The findings were accompanied by a comprehensive statement of how much better things might be if much more money, manpower, and commitment were available. The Joint Commission recommended, along with more outpatient services and smaller inpatient facilities, a general reorientation toward services that would be less disruptive of the patient's total life. In specific regard to rehabilitation as an aspect of service to the mentally ill, it recommended that

> . . . aftercare and rehabilitation [should be] essential parts of all service to mental patients, and the various methods of achieving rehabilitation should be integrated in all forms of services, among them day hospitals, night hospitals, aftercare clinics, public health nursing services, foster family care, convalescent nursing homes, rehabilitation centers, work services, and ex-patient groups. . . . It is important that rehabilitation be regarded as a part of a comprehensive program of patient services in which each and every member of the mental health team has a part to play.*

The report was successful in its purpose. It paved the way for a new federal program, enacted in 1963, providing support for building and meeting the payroll of new community-based treatment resources, modeled on the relatively few pioneering programs that had by then already accepted responsibility for designated local population groups, and were providing a comprehensive range of mental health services to them. By the end of the decade, 383 different facilities had been awarded a total of 505 construction and staffing grants, and the number of fully operational community mental health centers, as the new facilities are called, had passed 200.

Great progress was made during this same period in expanding mental illness benefits in private health insurance policies. As the number of general hospital psychiatric units grew, with their typically brief periods of treatment, agitation grew for insurance coverage of mental illness, which had previously been excluded from most health insurance policies. The response came slowly and gradually, in many cases providing no more than three weeks of inpatient care and no benefits at all for other forms of care. Meanwhile the average stay in general hospital psychiatric units steadily declined, and the economic feasibility of providing insurance coverage was proved; furthermore, the desirability of providing outpatient treatment that in many cases would obviate the need for, or reduce the duration of, inpatient care came to be realized. By 1970

*Joint Commission on Mental Illness and Health: *Action for Mental Health*. Basic Books, New York, 1961.

there were at least 120 million persons with private health insurance that provided at least a limited amount of psychiatric care—and for perhaps 30 million people, fairly extensive coverage. Most of this treatment has taken place in general hospital psychiatric units. In fact, by the time the federal Community Mental Health Centers Act was passed, in 1963, there were already more psychiatric admissions to general hospital psychiatric units than there were to state hospitals.

IN THE FACE of these encouraging accomplishments, we must also note the concurrent problems that were mounting in the large, traditional state hospitals—and, more recently, the considerable degree to which these problems have been ameliorated.

The census of the state hospitals grew steadily during the first half of the century—from 144,000 in 1903, when statistics were first kept, to 559,000 in 1955, when the census reached its all-time high. (The only decline was during a two-year period during World War II, when the census dropped slightly.) As the result of several factors—the increase in community treatment resources, a growing trend to find nursing homes and foster homes for deteriorated older people who perhaps should never have been in state hospitals at all, and probably most important, the new medications—the census began to drop in 1956. It has declined steadily since then. The largest single drop came between 1968 and 1969, when it fell to 367,000. It would be a mistake to underestimate the magnitude of this accomplishment; if the census had continued to grow at the same rate as in 1940 to 1955, there would be in 1970 some 721,000 people in state mental hospitals, whereas in actuality the census has declined by 34 percent during a time when the population of the country increased by 23 percent. Perhaps the most startling single indication of what the state hospitals have accomplished is seen in the release rate. As recently as 1945, the net live release rate per thousand resident patients was only 158 per year; by 1968, the figure had grown to 850.

THUS, DURING HALF A CENTURY mental health interests have progressed toward providing a more adequate amount of service to people whose lives are distressed and impaired by mental illness; toward proving the efficacy of immediately available community-based treatment; toward reducing the pile-up of chronically ill patients in the state hospitals.

It would be astonishing if all this had come about without many problems and complications including a certain amount of resistance from the caregivers themselves. Inevitably there has been a degree of rivalry and lack of understanding between community-based programs and state hospitals. The somatic assumptions of medication-centered treatment and a growing concern with the everyday "real life" problems of people with mental illness seem to have eroded the enthusiasm of an earlier generation for insight-oriented, "dynamic" formulations. At the same time, a number of training facilities have remained curiously unresponsive to such new forms of treatment as group therapy and family therapy and to the importance of community support resources such as day hospitals, halfway houses, and work training programs.

But the winds of change are unmistakably blowing. If there can be sufficient federal, state, and local funds marshalled to meet the attendant costs, it seems likely that a humane and socially useful approach to serving the mentally ill and enabling them to lead more productive lives in the community than has been possible before will be realized within the coming generation. In the midst of struggle to develop and finance more of the new types of facilities, there seems to be emerging a greater concern both about the *quality* of treatment and the quality of the *total life* of the person who has been mentally ill. Mental health professionals are coming to realize that it is a necessity, not a luxury or an option, to be concerned about enabling those who are or have been mentally ill to lead lives that give them some satisfaction and at the same time contribute usefully to the society at large.

IN THIS RESPECT, and with particular reference to this study, it is important to realize that the 1960's saw the emergence of the first large-scale attempts to rehabilitate the mentally ill. We shall have more to say about this later, but let us note at this point the growth in the number of people with a mental illness diagnosis who met the "closure" criteria of state vocational rehabilitation programs.* In 1959 there were only 3600 such closures. By 1968 the number had grown to more than 40,000—and the mental illness category had become the modal category.

---

*The term "closure" is used by vocational rehabilitation programs to mean "successfully closed." Closure is generally based upon the client's completion of a stipulated period of time in employment. The periods of time used by various states, and some of the problems arising therefrom, are discussed at several points later on.

II. Why and How the Study Was Done

THE JOINT INFORMATION SERVICE, from the earliest days of the federal community mental health center program, has subscribed to its goals, as have its sponsoring agencies. It has conducted a series of studies (listed on p. ii) of various aspects of community-based services for the mentally ill. These have been carried out by identifying outstanding programs, visiting them to observe and to conduct interviews, then writing up their experiences, in the hope that by doing so the knowledge of the problems they have experienced and the successes they have realized will be helpful to newer programs still in the process of planning or getting into operation.

AS WE VISITED SCORES OF FACILITIES over a period of years, we became concerned about the lack of emphasis on maintenance resources within the community. This concern originated from our belief that many of the people who have a history of mental illness require some special services that by and large are unneeded by the general population. We are saying that many of those who have experienced mental illness, particularly those with schizophrenia, have some identifiable problems in living that appear to be related to or originating from the illness.

• Many who have been patients in state mental hospitals have marked difficulties in establishing and maintaining successful mutual interdependencies. Consequently, if one hopes to enable them to survive in the general society, it seems necessary to create special arrangements and opportunities for the social interactions that we acknowledge to be a necessary ingredient of a meaningful life.

• Many seem ill-equipped to find and keep jobs. Many have never acquired any marketable skills. Of those who have, the skills have often fallen into disuse during the time of illness. Frequently there are large gaps in their vocational histories, making prospective employers wary of taking a chance on them. And knowledge on the employer's part of the applicant's history of mental illness would in many cases preclude his hiring him.

• Many do not have anyone to live with. Those who have not been extruded from their families often have families too turbulent and disorganized for the patient's well-being. Many do not have the financial resources or credit rating to take apartments on their own. They run the risk of settling into single rooms in dilapidated rooming houses or residential hotels, where they may be exploited by their landlords.

THESE ARE NOT ALL THE PROBLEMS in living that afflict many of the people who have had serious mental illness, but they illustrate our concern. Thus, we observed that the very progress that had enabled treating facilities to send people back into the community quickly, or to retain them there without ever sending them into total institutions, had at the same time resulted in the accumulation of tens of thousands of people who were living marginal lives in the community, frequently relapsing with resultant rehospitalization. To put it another way, we became increasingly convinced that if treating facilities have committed themselves to retaining patients in the community, they must also commit themselves to a spectrum of services that will enhance the likelihood that the patient will be able to remain there, living a life worth something to himself and to the community.

THERE IS EVIDENCE that our concern is justified. At the same time that state hospitals have been reducing their census and their length of stay for new admissions, the proportion of readmissions has steadily risen. In 38 states, readmissions in 1968 comprised more than thirty percent of all admissions. To oversimplify only a little, this means that of those who are admitted to state hospitals, about a third are a group of patients who come and go. They reconstitute in the hospital, return to the community, and relapse. The relapse may often be related to the illness process and not to the quality of their lives in the community; but from what we have heard and seen, we believe that very often it is not the result of the illness but rather the lack of a satisfactory arrangement for living and working.

Some research buttresses this belief. Freeman and Simmons* in 1963 published a one-year follow-up study of 649 mental patients in Massachusetts, based on interviews with family members regarding the success or failure of the patient in remaining in the community. They found the patient typically assailed by a broad variety of problems in living, and

---

*H. E. Freeman and O. G. Simmons: *The Mental Patient Comes Home.* John Wiley and Sons, Inc., New York, 1963.

they found that one third returned to the hospital within the one year of the study. During that year only about half of the "successes" and 30 percent of the "failures" worked more than half time. About a quarter lived in isolation.

Helen Ellis,† a sociologist, examined the status of 112 patients discharged from New Mexico State Hospital and found that no more than 25 to 30 percent of the patients appeared to be "on the road to recovery." About 30 percent appeared to have deteriorated since leaving the hospital.

W E ARE NOT SAYING that there has been no interest or activity in developing the community resources that many of the mentally ill need. Chapter IV describes the growth that has taken place, particularly during the 1960's. There is obviously a growing awareness of the need. But our two principal persuasions in undertaking this study were borne out by what we heard in the course of our field work.

• Many mental health professionals do not have much knowledge of, interest in, or commitment to the importance of rehabilitative and supporting resources that must be available on an intermediate or long-term basis to the seriously ill people that they seek to retain in the community. This is perhaps most particularly the result of the lack of emphasis in training programs on the supporting and maintaining aspects of chronic illness. We agree with Bernard Rubin* that "attention to rehabilitation . . . is unusual and the lack of concern with it has been a major failing of the mental health professionals."

• Despite the increasing numbers of mentally ill being served in federal-state vocational rehabilitation programs, and the growth in numbers of such community resources as halfway houses, the population needing such services has grown even faster. Since the number of supporting resources has not grown fast enough, a higher priority needs to be assigned to this aspect of comprehensive mental health services.

A S OF MID-1970, of 210 federally funded community mental health centers in operation, 160 had agreed to provide rehabilitation services through one or more community agencies. Since rehabilitation, under the requirements of the federally supported program, is one of the additional services rather than one of the five "essential" services required

†H. H. Ellis: "The Patient on Leave: A Qualified Success Story," *Mental Hospitals* 13:9:491-493, September 1962.

*B. Rubin: "Community Psychiatry," *Archives of General Psychiatry* 20:5:497-507, May 1969.

for funding eligibility, no intensive examination of the kinds and amounts of rehabilitation has yet been undertaken. Most of the indicated services are provided by state vocational rehabilitation services. Others represent the availability of resources such as sheltered workshops operated by Goodwill Industries, to which the centers could refer patients.

In any event, the National Institute of Mental Health, immediately responsive to our concern about the need for greater emphasis on rehabilitation services, agreed to support a year's study of such programs as part of the continuing cost-sharing contract under which the Joint Information Service has been studying community-based mental health services.

It did not seem possible in such a short time to carry out a field study of the several forms that rehabilitation services have taken, principally sheltered workshops, ex-patient clubs, and halfway houses. Consequently we decided to investigate two different types of facilities: halfway houses, which will be the subject of a separate report, and a group of facilities that call themselves *psychosocial rehabilitation centers*. Our interest in the latter arose from our personal knowledge of the two largest such facilities, Fountain House in New York and Horizon House in Philadelphia.

We were proceeding from our assumption that three of the main needs of a large group of the seriously mentally ill are in the areas of *a*) socialization training and socializing opportunities, *b*) work, and *c*) living arrangements. Existing resources do not divide discretely in scope among these three areas. For example, Gutman Rehabilitation Programs, Inc., in Portland, Oregon, is an example of a group of halfway houses by definition concerned with living arrangements but nonetheless placing great emphasis on recruiting jobs; the COVE program in Everett, Washington, is an example of a rehabilitation service whose core emphasis is job placement but which also provides patients with a temporary residence; and so on through a variety of patterns. We selected the psychosocial centers in the belief that their experiences would be important, since each provides some attention to all three of our primary areas of concern.

We anticipated that there would be few such comprehensive programs and that we would have difficulty in identifying them. We began by consulting Horizon House and Fountain House. Each furnished an essentially similar list of fellow agencies. We contacted these additional programs, asking them in turn to tell us of any others that they knew about. Eventually we had developed a list of thirteen more or less comprehensive centers. There may be others that fit the definition, but if so they are not known to any of the thirteen that we dealt with.

To each such center we sent a brief "identifying" questionnaire (Appendix II). The responses were such as to enable us to divide them into two groups, principally on the basis of size; six of the programs were large enough in terms of staff and client load to appear to fall within our purpose. The other six, some of them operating only part time and with only one or two staff members, seemed too small.* Curiously, only one of the thirteen was located west of the Mississippi.

The directors of the six selected for field visits readily agreed to participate in the study. They were asked to complete an orientation questionnaire (Appendix III) somewhat lengthier than the first one, thus allowing the authors to study the background characteristics of the agencies in advance of the visits. Two-day visits were scheduled to each facility, with the authors participating as follows:

	Glasscote	Cumming	Rutman	Sussex	Glassman
Fountain House, New York	x	x	x	x	x
Horizon House, Philadelphia	x	x		x	x
Council House, Pittsburgh	x	x	x	x	
Hill House, Cleveland	x	x	x	x	
Portals, Los Angeles	x	x	x		x
Thresholds, Chicago	x	x	x		x

During these visits we were able to interview all staff members at the last four programs listed. At Horizon House and Fountain House, which have significantly larger staffs, we asked the directors to select approximately 15 staff members from whom they felt we could get a representative picture and a good understanding of the philosophy, goals, and operations of the agency.

At each of the programs we also interviewed at least two clients, and we were able to meet large groups of clients at Hill House and Portals.

The visits took place during the last quarter of 1969. Following the visits, a conference was held in Washington, attended by four of the

---

*With one exception: the Center Club in Boston was approximately the same size as Portals; but Portals was chosen because it was the only center in the western part of the country. A thirteenth program was identified in Canada— Montreal's Forward House, which was represented at the conference described below.

five authors, representatives of the six facilities we had visited, and five additional persons representing all but two of the smaller centers which we did not include in the field study.* At this time we pursued an agenda based on the issues and the problems that we felt we had discerned during our visits to the facilities.

Both the field visits and the conference were recorded and the tapes transcribed. The authors prepared field trip reports following each visit. All of this material was then processed as the basis for the individual program descriptions contained herein, and the conference proceedings served largely as the basis for the viewpoints set forth in Chapter XII.

Concurrently a search of the literature of rehabilitation was undertaken by the Joint Information Service staff, working from *Psychological Abstracts, Index Medicus, Rehabilitation Literature,* and bibliographies and other materials furnished by the National Clearinghouse for Mental Health Information. This served as a major component of the portions of the report that attempt to define and construct a theory for rehabilitation and to exemplify the rehabilitation efforts that have taken place mainly during the past dozen years.

---

*Bridgehaven in Louisville was unable to send a representative. Prospect House in East Orange, New Jersey, was not invited, because it was in process of changing directors.

III. Toward a Definition and a Theory

THE ELUSIVENESS OF THE TERM REHABILITATION was perhaps as well described in 1953 by Charlotte Green Schwartz* as it has ever been. She considered a number of then current statements variously identifying rehabilitation *a*) as the services, techniques, or organization of effort necessary to bring about functional restoration of a patient; *b*) as the process by which handicapped persons improve and develop their personal equipment and capacities for satisfactory living within their environment; *c*) as the restoration of the handicapped to the fullest physical, mental, social, vocational, and economic usefulness of which they are capable; *d*) as human adjustment of the whole personality; *e*) as reintegration of the individual into the community; *f*) as the restoration of creative ability and of the will to create. She concludes that

> definitions of rehabilitation . . . are so generalized that it is difficult to use them in program planning and development.

She added that there did not seem to be a clearly delimited body of rehabilitation literature.

In 1959, Bertram Black,† a pioneer in sheltered workshop services for the mentally ill and for many years the director of the ALTRO Workshops in New York City, described rehabilitation as

> aimed at returning the handicapped person to as much usefulness in society as his remaining capabilities will allow.

In 1963 a joint committee of the Public Health Service and the Vocational Rehabilitation Administration (now the Social and Rehabilitation Service) held a conference to discuss area-wide planning of rehabilitation facilities. It formulated a definition of rehabilitation as

> the process of restoring the disabled to optimal physical, mental, social, vocational, and economic usefulness.

---

*C. G. Schwartz: *Rehabilitation of Mental Hospital Patients: Review of the Literature.* Public Health Service Publication No. 297, 1953.
†B. J. Black: "The Protected Workshop in the Rehabilitation of the Mentally Ill," *Psychiatric Quarterly, Supplement* 33:107-108, 1959.

This is quite close to Mrs. Schwartz's definition *c*) above, which is the formulation of the National Rehabilitation Association.

Douglas Bennett, an English psychiatrist long concerned with rehabilitation, subscribes to a definition he attributes to Dr. Frank S. Cooksey.

> Rehabilitation is the process of enabling a handicapped person to make the best possible use of his residual capacities in as normal a social context as possible.*

Somewhat earlier, Dr. Bennett, together with Drs. J. K. Wing and John Denham, had formulated a definition of rehabilitation as it applies in the industrial rehabilitation of long-stay schizophrenic patients.

> [Rehabilitation is] any activity which aims at preventing or reducing secondary handicaps, or at developing compensatory mechanisms for irreducible primary or secondary handicaps.

One of the best discussions of rehabilitation which we have encountered is a report of the proceedings of a conference on psychological research and rehabilitation, sponsored by the American Psychological Association.† Dr. Lofquist asserts that

> Whatever definition of rehabilitation is favored by a particular person or group, perhaps all would agree that: *a*) rehabilitation is concerned with practical problems in the lives of individuals; *b*) it is concerned with past, present, and future individual behavior, and with assisting an individual to find an optimal balance of these which will permit living as well as possible within the handicaps imposed by disability and within the potential development described by the individual's particular balance sheet of plus and minus ability, aptitude, interest, and personality factors; and *c*) it involves active interprofessional participation in planning with and for the individual.

THE QUESTION, OF COURSE, is one of determining when a particular individual has, in fact, reached his highest potential. Instruments available for measurement seem to be of limited usefulness. The process may often be one of trial and error. There seem to be two principal criteria that have universal acceptance: *a*) is the person working? and *b*) is he living in a reasonably autonomous way in an appropriate setting in the community? Emphasis on work has been very strong, for a variety of understandable reasons. A high value is placed on work in our society,

---

*Quoted in "The Organization of Psychiatric Rehabilitation Services," unpublished, dated August 1968.

†L. H. Lofquist (ed.): *Psychological Research and Rehabilitation.* American Psychological Association, Washington, D.C., 1961.

and to be usefully employed is one of the yardsticks whereby we judge whether a given individual is adequate. This value has been specifically enhanced within the history of rehabilitation in this country; most of the support and development of rehabilitation services has been under the direction and funding of the federal rehabilitation program, which until very recently has equated being rehabilitated with being employed. This was inherent even in the name of the agency, which was known, successively, as the Office of Vocational Rehabilitation and then, when it moved to a more independent status, the Vocational Rehabilitation Administration. Only in recent years has the almost exclusive emphasis on employment been somewhat broadened, as evidenced by the change of name in 1967 to the Social and Rehabilitation Service.

The importance of work within the federal program is attested by a training manual* that defines "the rehabilitation process":

> The rehabilitation process consists of a planned, orderly sequence of services related to the total needs of the handicapped individual. It is a process built around the problems of a handicapped individual and the attempts of the vocational rehabilitation counselor to help solve these problems and thus to bring about the *vocational* adjustment of the handicapped person.
>
> The process begins with the initial casefinding or referral, and ends with the successful placement of the handicapped individual on a job. The unique characteristic that distinguishes and differentiates the vocational rehabilitation process from all other forms of counseling is its primary objective, which is the realistic and permanent *vocational* adjustment of the handicapped individual. To accomplish the vocational adjustment, a wide range of services is provided.
>
> Services are obtained, often by purchase, from virtually the full span of community resources, depending on individual needs. Private physicians, public and private educational institutions, and employers are but some of the resources which are regularly drawn into effective rehabilitation.

HAROLD R. MARTIN in 1957 made a suggestion† that we think is of the utmost importance and which has particular relevance to the approach we used in this study. He said that

---

*J. F. McGowan and T. L. Porter: *An Introduction to the Vocational Rehabilitation Process.* Social and Rehabilitation Service, U.S. Department of Health, Education, and Welfare, Washington, D.C., 1967.

†M. Greenblatt (ed.): *Rehabilitation of the Mentally Ill.* American Association for the Advancement of Science, Washington, D. C., 1959.

most definitions of rehabilitation tend to be generalized and all-encompassing. In theory, the term would include the specific therapies; however, that is inconsistent with usage. It is proposed that *rehabilitation* be used when referring to activities which attempt to discover and develop the patient's assets in contrast to *treatment,* which is a direct attack on the patient's disability.

We agree with Dr. Martin. We have tended throughout this study to differentiate treatment of illness from support and development of an individual's potential for autonomous living, in numerous cases even in the continued presence of the illness. Some will feel that our conception is too narrow, but if it seems so, at least we feel it is more precise than the common tendency to label everything that goes on within a hospital as "rehabilitation." We maintain that to give a patient an antipsychotic medication is to treat his illness; to habituate him to coming to work on time is to rehabilitate him. We suspect that among those who have no conception of what rehabilitation is *not* are some who simply have not come to grips with the problem of what rehabilitation *is*. In any case, this will help to explain our view that such facilities as halfway houses to live in, sheltered workshops or special job placements to work in, and social clubs to socialize in are in essence rehabilitating, while aftercare clinics and day hospitals are in essence treating. This is not to say that treating and rehabilitating should be either sequential or carried out by separate institutions. Good state hospitals today attempt, as we understand their efforts, both to treat and to rehabilitate simultaneously, and so do the more advanced community mental health centers.

A FURTHER DESCRIPTION of the federal-state rehabilitation program will be presented later. Let us simply observe here that the program should not be faulted for its strong emphasis on employment, since to get the handicapped to work was precisely the purpose for which the program was created in 1920, and this is largely the mandate under which it has operated up to the present time.

For the purposes of the mentally ill, we think it is not broad enough. Not all of the people who are impaired by mental illness and/or the experience of having lived for many years in a state hospital will be capable of becoming employed, either competitively or in a program of sheltered employment. Some are too old, too frail physically, too disordered mentally. But among these are a number of people who do not seem to need to be in mental hospitals; despite the fact that they may not be productive, they can still, with some assistance, meet the demands of day-to-day living in the community without harm to themselves or to others.

Some have asked why one should make the effort to return such people to the community, or to retain them there rather than transferring them to mental hospitals. In other words, Are they not as well off or better off in the mental hospital as they would be anywhere? In particular cases, for example, when the mental hospital is a very good one and the resources of the community are particularly poor, the answer might be yes. As a general principle, both of what is best for the individual and what it behooves a humane society to provide for handicapped people, the answer ought to be no. Even though many people voluntarily institutionalize themselves, as in the military or in religious orders, the circumstances surrounding hospitalization for mental illness are usually quite different—rarely truly voluntary (even though the form of commitment may in a legal sense be "voluntary"), but rather the result of social breakdown, or coercion by relatives, or because of behavior found threatening or offensive to the community. In short, as a social policy, it seems appropriate to plan for and provide the necessary resources to people handicapped by mental illness, or by residuals of mental illness, so that they may be contained within the general society rather than in total institutions. Thus, we would include within our conception of rehabilitation the provision of service, perhaps permanently, to some people who will "top off" at too low a level to work.

Webster* defines *rehabilitate* as "to *restore* to a condition of health or useful and constructive activity." But many of the people who are referred to rehabilitation services do not seem to have anything much to rehabilitate. In visiting the psychosocial centers, we heard time and again that they were dealing with many clients, perhaps the majority, who had never acquired the basic day-to-day skills of social interaction and personal maintenance, and who had never acquired any marketable skills. It was heartening to us that the programs were serving some such people. However, the fact that they are being "habilitated" (defined by Webster as "to qualify oneself") rather than restored to some previous level of functioning has important implications for the nature of the rehabilitation experience that one plans for them.

B ASED BOTH ON OUR OWN OBSERVATIONS and on the definitions set forth above, we would define rehabilitation as

the process of enabling an impaired person to renew old skills or to acquire new skills that will qualify him to live in the general society

---

Webster's Third New International Dictionary. G. & C. Merriam Co., Springfield, Mass., 1965.

to the greatest extent that his particular condition and circumstances will allow. This will include as an ideal goal full-time competitive employment, plus residence in some appropriate setting that allows for reasonable autonomy, plus the development of some successful mutual interdependencies. But for many who can nonetheless be considered rehabilitated, it may allow only limited, noncompetitive employment, or no employment at all; the need to live in a specialized residence such as a halfway house; and the need for specially constructed socialization opportunities.

IT SEEMS NECESSARY TO NOTE at this point that while many of the people with mental illness could benefit from rehabilitation services, many others do not appear to need them. It is always a mistake to conceive of mental illness as a single entity, since it assumes many forms; the *Diagnostic and Statistical Manual of Mental Disorders* sets forth a dozen different *major* categories of mental illness.* Some rather large ones, notably the depressions, often occur in people who have already become educationally, socially, and vocationally adequate, and once the typically brief illness has cleared they are typically able to resume their previous work and social relationships. The same is true of some schizophrenics. When Council House, one of the facilities described herein, conducted a survey of people, most of whom were schizophrenics, who had refused or dropped out of its services, they found that about a third had made a community adjustment without the need of specific support resources; another third had made an adjustment by finding some kind of support from other than a mental health agency; while a third were "too sick" to avail themselves of the psychosocial center's services (see pp. 81-82).

What seems important is that in each case there be a determination of whether the person appears to require special support resources in order to overcome any deficit that may arise from or follow upon his illness.

WE ATTEMPTED FROM THE OUTSET to identify theories of rehabilitation as it was practiced in the programs that we visited. For the most part we were not successful. We were impressed with each of the centers in terms of attitudes toward clients, inventiveness, and initiative, but as a group the staff emerge as program-oriented pragmatists and not as theoreticians. (Fountain House has a carefully worked out family

---

*Exclusive of alcoholism, drug dependence, sexual deviations, and various other conditions not usually conceived of as "serious mental illness."

analogy, but it is less a theoretical construction of rehabilitation than a vehicle for expressing a caring attitude toward clients.)

Nonetheless, there is a unifying, even if largely unarticulated, common belief among the centers, which we can identify as residing in the educational model. In each program there is a deliberate de-emphasis of symptoms and of thought disorder, amounting in many cases almost to a denial that the client is or has been sick. "We work with the healthy portions of the ego" is a statement that we heard time and again.

Thus, the concern is to teach the clients in a variety of ways such things as how to groom themselves appropriately, how to ride on buses, how to get to events on time, how to shop for food, how to plan and cook a meal, how to behave in a work setting. If the particular client has been rendered symptomless by psychiatric treatment, by the natural healing properties of the organism, or by anything else, well and good. But even if he is still persuaded that his head is full of wires or that his body is full of microphones, he can be taught to behave in ways that will allow him to live in, rather than to be extruded from, the general society. If he cannot be dissuaded from his delusions, or if his hallucinations continue despite his medication regimen, he can be taught not to reveal his symptoms to others.*

The programs have not anticipated a successful outcome with every client, particularly since they are working by and large with people that one program director described as "the throwaways." How well each has succeeded is difficult to say, since many of the variables have not been measured. But there have been startling successes in individual cases, and the programs seem nurtured by these outstanding examples and sustained in their willingness to press on.

WALTER BARTON † in his book *Administration in Psychiatry* presents a clinical descriptive rationale for rehabilitation, from which the following is extracted.

Participation in a program of activities and work while in the hospital

---

*This approach was well expressed a decade ago by C. A. Roberts, a psychiatrist: "Our objective in treatment is not to make sure that a schizophrenic no longer has delusions or hallucinations, but rather to be sure that his behavior will be socially acceptable. Many of our so-called cured schizophrenics still have delusions but they have learned not to act on the basis of them and can function in an acceptable manner." From "Rehabilitation of the Mentally Ill" in *Mental Hospitals* 11:4:9-12, December 1960.

†W. E. Barton: *Administration in Psychiatry*. Charles C. Thomas, Springfield, Ill., 1962.

helps to prepare the patient to live in the community. . . . There is room for criticism of the activities program of most public psychiatric hospitals. Preparation for life in the real world of most patients is not made possible through a program of games, sports, or handicrafts. The unskilled laborer and the lower social classes predominate among the hospitalized, although all social groups and occupations are represented among the acute mentally ill. Tossing a bean bag or roller skating may start a patient moving smoothly and these simple events may have served to establish a relationship with a therapist, but the activities are not necessarily sufficient preparation for return to a job. *The change to a useful work program and to a leisure time schedule likely to be practical later on should come as early in the program of therapy as the patient can manage it. . . .*

To return to productive community life, the chronic mental patient must give up a stable hospital adjustment for an anxiety-evoking, uncertain future. . . . The family, and there may be none, may indicate by its soul-searing rejection that there is no place for the patient any longer. . . . *It is a long step for a patient to take if he must live alone and find a job in a tight employment market with skills dulled after years of disuse.* And if isolation and loneliness, and uncertainty about one's ability to hold a job, were not handicap enough, the hostile community attitudes toward the ex-mental patient must be faced. "He just got out of the state hospital, you can't tell what he will do next"; "he may crack up again when the pressure is on" are milder comments that reflect the bitter outcome "at home". . . .

The primary motivating force towards more active social participation derives from the warmth, sincerity, and interest of others. . . .

The dependency upon staff and hospital that characterizes the relationship of many chronically ill mental patients may be broken by a series of transitional steps between hospital and community. . . .

Chronic mental patients usually require a long and intensive period of work to effect successful rehabilitation. Whereas a four to six weeks' period may be quite long enough to evaluate and place an acute mental patient, those who have been mentally ill for years seldom begin to show improvement in less than six to eight months, and *two to three years of effort may be required to reach a satisfactory rehabilitation goal.* Women seem to take longer than men to respond.

In 1960, the anthropologist David Landy, who has done much work in the area of mental illness, served, along with Henry Wechsler, as editor of a special section of the *Journal of Social Issues,* devoted to rehabilitation of the mentally ill. This issue examined ex-patient clubs, halfway houses, and other transitional facilities.

In an article called "Rehabilitation as a Sociocultural Process,"* Landy speaks of the rehabilitation process as one of *acculturation*. After a patient has accepted the enforced cultural conformity required in the hospital, as his symptoms remit, as he begins to accept more "normal" ways of behaving, he may be considered for return to the community. But if he lacks money, family, friends, and social adaptational techniques, then he may require the service of one or more types of transitional facilities whose purpose is to enhance his capabilities to live autonomously in the community.

From the patient's viewpoint, the process can be termed *resocialization*, or, for those who must acquire certain behaviors for the first time, *socialization*. However, socialization process for the patient must not be confused with socialization of the child. The patient

> already has some experience, however his growing may have been a pathologically distorted process, in learning the ways of his society and reference groups. No matter how deprived he may have been, no matter how asocial a warped socialization may have rendered him, he is not simply facing life *de novo*. . . . Authority figures (staff personnel) and peer group figures (fellow patients) serve, therefore, not only as direct teachers or inculcators but as role models for the proper relearning of older roles, or the learning of newer, more socially appropriate, more "adult" roles.

But the patient has in common with the child that the end point or major goal of socialization is "the internalization of the values and practices which define and direct his culture. When he has been able to internalize these values and practices, he has also identified with authority figures and peers. . . . Identification then means that the individual has learned how to behave like the person or persons with whom he identifies and is capable of such behavior *in the absence of the persons who acted as teachers and models.*" Thus, those who direct the socialization process become *models*—positive or negative—with whom the patient identifies.

THE MOST EXTENSIVE DISCUSSION we have seen of the use in rehabilitation of an educational, and, more specifically, learning theory, model is the above-mentioned proceedings of the 1960 American Psychological Association conference on research and rehabilitation. This conference appears to have been concerned essentially with physical dis-

---

*D. Landy: "Rehabilitation as a Sociocultural Process," *Journal of Social Issues* 16:2:3-7, April 1960.

ability and only incidentally with mental disability, but much that was put forward as principle seems to have applicability to rehabilitation programs for the mentally ill.

> One participant [unidentified] stated that rehabilitation lends itself to the exploitation of about five major heavyweight principles: reinforcement, extinction, discrimination, generalization, and counterconditioning of incompatible responses. There are effective behavioral methods . . . that are straightforward applications of these principles. Some reports are already in the literature showing the success of these methods and these principles in the study and treatment of individuals who are mentally retarded, autistic, deaf, psychotic, neurotic, and speech defective. . . . These behavioral approaches seem not to be used by rehabilitation counselors and therapists, and it may be helpful to communicate them.

> If the learning group has anything to offer to the field of rehabilitation, it is a strong statement that behavior is a function of environmental variables which can be manipulated and utilized. The layman's view that behavior is internally controlled and mediated by verbalized understanding is probably badly in need of correction or supplementation.

> Many problems in rehabilitation seem to stem from attempts to change people's behavior by telling or explaining something to them rather than altering the reinforcing environment. If the person doesn't understand, it is thought that the behavior can't be changed. If he does understand, then he should do what is requested of him, and therapists are puzzled when the appropriate behavior is not forthcoming. *They appear not to know that many complex performances can be accomplished by people who may not understand what they are doing in the sense of being able to verbalize those performances or the reasons for their own behavior.* Needless failure in rehabilitation occurs when a person is said to be too unmotivated, too stupid, too stubborn, or too psychotic to behave in a desired way.

Said another [also unidentified] participant, regarding the "institutional neurosis" associated with state hospitals:

> . . . the individual who becomes chronically ill . . . has a marked change in his system of reinforcement. Many learned social and primary reinforcers are withdrawn, and the main task may come to be a consideration of a way of reinstituting a system of reinforcers so that desired types of behaviors can be shaped up.

Dr. Emory L. Cowen strikes at the problem of a theoretical approach to disability (and thus rehabilitation) when he asserts that a more comprehensive psychological theory of disability may not be needed since there is no systematic evidence of known psychological differences between the disabled and nondisabled.

> On the basis of presently available observations and empirical findings, there is little reason to believe either that such evidence is available or that it is likely to be established in the foreseeable future. Overlap rather than difference between disabled and nondisabled groups seems to be a governing principle.

We should add to the above some principles which Mrs. Schwartz* identified among a number of rehabilitation efforts taking place in mental hospitals in the 1950's.

• Those who are attempting to bring about the rehabilitation of the patient must determine his existing ability and then develop experiences which fit it.

• There appears to be general agreement that in order to work effectively with mental patients, personnel must accept the present functioning level of the patient.

• The object of participating with the patient is to move him from the level at which he functions to the next level of functioning.

She cites the following attitudes toward patients as having rehabilitative effects:

• Respect for and acceptance of the patient and his present way of functioning (including a lack of fear of the patient's hostility and other "symptoms").

• Hopefulness concerning the patient's ability to change and confidence in the development of his abilities.

• Approval, reassurance, and support for what the patient is able to do at the moment.

• Alertness to the patient's needs and attempts to fulfill these needs, with the attitude of giving without demanding any return—not using the patient to fill the staff member's needs.

• Affection and intimacy, personal interest, concern, and understanding.

• Patience and encouragement concerning the patient's progress, however slow.

• Permissiveness (selective, not laissez-faire), expressed by lack of censure or embarrassment concerning unconventional behavior, making it clear to the patient, however, that the behavior is not necessarily approved.

---

*C. G. Schwartz: *Rehabilitation of Mental Hospital Patients: Review of the Literature*. Public Health Service Publication No. 297, 1953.

• Encouragement of the patient to accept as much responsibility as he can handle at present, giving him as much freedom and room for spontaneity as he can manage, though at the same time providing him with protection from his own impulses and a feeling of security by a firm, tactful, consistent, and reliable response from the staff member.

• Attempts to understand the meaning of the patient's behavior.

THESE ARE THE PRINCIPAL EFFORTS we have found at formulating a theory of rehabilitation. None of them appeared to feel that their efforts were definitive, or even particularly satisfactory. As Landy expressed it:

> . . . the field of psychiatric rehabilitation [has] as yet been unable to provide an adequate theoretical framework for the study and description of the rehabilitation process; but one must be provided before that part of the rehabilitative process concerning the patient's departure from the mental hospital and re-entrance into the community is to be understood.

A decade later, the state-of-the-art in theory of rehabilitating the mentally ill may not have moved a great deal forward, in the opinion of one of our authors (Rutman), who said, in the course of our visit to Horizon House:

> All of the existing efforts are well-intentioned but intuitive efforts to make people more comfortable in the community. If there is a process or sequence of some unique combination of services, so far no one has adequately identified or documented it. In the present revision of our own program, we are attempting to construct something that we hope will do that. We have put a new program together out of experience and common sense, not from a formulated theory.

ONE POINT ON WHICH PRACTICALLY EVERYONE who has written about rehabilitation agrees is that the process should be started as soon as the person becomes ill. This obviously must be in many cases hypothetical rather than a practical reality, since the point at which one becomes ill is often difficult to ascertain; more important, many of those whom we call mentally ill do not come to the attention of treating resources because they are ill but rather because their illness has reached the point of causing them to become troublesome. In any case, scarcely anyone believes that rehabilitation efforts should be postponed until the time of discharge from the hospital. A number of state hospitals that have come to place emphasis on rehabilitation assert that the rehabilitation process begins "on the day of admission."

IV. How Rehabilitation Has Developed in the United States

THE SOCIAL AND REHABILITATION SERVICE, as the federal rehabilitation program has been known since 1967, traces the beginnings of interest in rehabilitation of the physically handicapped back to the 1860's, but during the following several decades there was little forward movement. The best demarcation date for an overview of the program as it exists today is probably 1918, when the Soldiers Rehabilitation Act was passed, providing vocational rehabilitation services to

> any disabled veteran who was unable to carry on a gainful occupation, to resume his former occupation, or to enter upon some other occupation, or having resumed or entered upon such occupation was unable to continue the same successfully.

Even at the time of debating the provisions of this bill, there was some sentiment within Congress to include disabled civilians. Two years later the Civilian Vocational Rehabilitation Act of 1920 was passed, "stimulated by the success of the Soldiers Rehabilitation Act." The civilian program provided federal funds to match state funds on an equal basis, to be used to provide vocational guidance, training, "occupation adjustment," prosthetics, and placement services. The program was temporary but was extended several times until 1935, when it was established on a permanent basis.

The first of three major pieces of legislation broadening the federal program of grants to the states came in 1943, at which time the word "physically" was deleted from the act, thereby making the mentally handicapped eligible for service. This provision came about largely at the instigation of the late Dr. Winfred Overholser, who was superintendent of St. Elizabeths Hospital in Washington, D.C., and Dr. George S. Stevenson, a psychiatrist who at the time was director of what is now the National Association for Mental Health.

From the literature we can see that there were the beginning glimmers of interest in rehabilitating the mentally ill during this period. A bibliography of rehabilitation literature from 1940 through 1946* contains a large number of references to psychological and psychiatric aspects of rehabilitation of the physically handicapped, and a handful of references concerned directly with rehabilitating the mentally ill to the community.

In 1944 Olive E. Dorman described† the usefulness of outside employment as a tool in rehabilitation of patients at Worcester State Hospital. In the same year Thomas A. C. Rennie urged the need for national planning for psychiatric rehabilitation,‡ describing the size of the job and its social significance. Otto Kant asserted§ that "after underlying conflicts have been resolved, re-education is necessary for the social rehabilitation of the patients."

A year later Opal Fore described‖ the adjustment and earnings of the mentally ill in Iowa who had been "paroled," concluding that the state had been saved expense and that few of the patients had been returned to the hospital. John Davis wrote¶ of the principles and techniques of rehabilitating the mentally ill, including the role of the family, of occupational and recreational therapy, and of psychotherapy. And Minnie Fevold described** the benefits of a sheltered workshop for those afflicted with mental disorders.

But these must be viewed as pioneers; by and large a federal program for rehabilitating the mentally ill seems to have been an idea that came before its time. The new legislation gave the states the option of broadening their programs to include the mentally ill, and few did so. Even among those that did, little use was made of the new provision. Massachusetts, the first state to enact a rehabilitation program for the physi-

---

*M. Riviere: *Rehabilitation of the Handicapped*. National Council on Rehabilitation, 1949.

†O. E. Dorman: "Jobs for Mental Patients," *Survey Midmonthly* 80:115-117, April 1944.

‡T. A. C. Rennie: "The Need for National Planning for Psychiatric Rehabilitation," *American Journal of Orthopsychiatry* 14:386-394, July 1944.

§O. Kant: "Choice of Method in Psychotherapy," *Diseases of the Nervous System* 5:11:325-329, November 1944.

‖O. Fore: "An Experiment in Parole and Hospital Employment for the Mentally Ill in Iowa," *Mental Hygiene* 29:2:423-428, July 1945.

¶J. E. Davis: "An Introduction to the Problems of Rehabilitation," *Mental Hygiene* 29:217, April 1945.

**M. Fevold: "A Sheltered Workshop Program: The Contribution of Occupational Therapy in a Sheltered Program of Goodwill Industries," *Crippled Child* 23:1234-1240, December 1945.

cally handicapped (in 1921), had by 1955, twelve years after the mentally ill became eligible under the federal provisions, received only six referrals from state hospitals in the Boston area.* By 1956 the average number of psychiatric rehabilitations per state had risen only to twenty.†

In 1954 the federal legislation was once more broadened, making considerably more money available, making increased provision for purchasing training programs for clients, and adding research and demonstration projects. While this enhanced program did not make it mandatory for states to include the mentally ill, it greatly encouraged it. The Office of Vocational Rehabilitation, as it was then known, began a series of regional conferences specifically concerning rehabilitation of the mentally ill, to which many state hospital personnel were invited.

In 1965 the federal legislation was broadened again, establishing a uniform formula for federal funds to be provided to states, initially at 75 percent, later raised to 80 percent. (The amount allocated to each state is based on a traditional formula for federal matching programs which takes into account the state's population and per capita income.) The new amendments also made it possible for federal grants to be made directly to counties and cities, rather than exclusively on a statewide basis.

For the first time the program provided service to people who had been previously excluded on the grounds that there did not seem to be a clear present prospect for vocational capability. The mentally ill and the mentally retarded can now be provided service for as long as eighteen months if the state elects to do so. Following this "extended evaluation" period, as it is called, a determination is then made of whether the client does indeed possess a vocational potential that would qualify him for further training opportunities.

The project grant provision of the current legislation covers special grants of up to five years to states for two purposes: a) development of methods or techniques for providing services which are new in that state; and b) projects to serve people who have catastrophic or particularly severe disabilities. The formula calls for 90 percent federal funding for the first three years and 75 percent during the remaining two years.

---

*L. L. Havens and F. A. Harding: "Rehabilitating the Mentally Disabled: A Report of the Massachusetts Commission's Methods and Experience," *Journal of Rehabilitation* 27:6:22-23, 43-46, November-December 1961.

†S. S. Olshansky: "Vocational Rehabilitation and the Ex-Mental Patient," *Journal of Rehabilitation* 26:6:17-19, 40-45, November-December 1960.

Federal funds became available under the 1965 amendments for helping to meet the cost of building new rehabilitation centers and workshops, with the federal share ranging from one third to two thirds of the total cost—but as of 1970 no construction of facilities for the mentally ill had been funded under this provision.

Rehabilitation services for the mentally ill have seen by far their greatest growth since the enactment of the 1965 amendments. The great majority of the country's 275 state hospitals now have full-time rehabilitation counselors assigned to them. At least 25 state hospitals have full-fledged rehabilitation units on their grounds, intended to rehabilitate the patient while he is still hospitalized; typically these units have from three to ten rehabilitation counselors. Good examples are those at Norman, Oklahoma, Little Rock, Arkansas, Boston State Hospital, and the largest, with 200 beds, at Milledgeville, Georgia.

The successful "closures" of mental illness rehabilitation clients keep increasing both in numbers and as a portion of the total number of rehabilitations. In 1959 there were only 3600 mental illness closures, representing four percent of the total. By 1969 the number had risen to 54,500, representing 23 percent of the total. In 1968 mental illness rehabilitations became the modal category, for the first time surpassing the historic leading group, orthopedic deformities and impairments.

(For the purposes of this report, concerned as it is largely with rehabilitation of the patient with major mental illness, it is important to realize that only about a third of the successful mental illness closures are classed as psychotic disorders. Almost as many—thirty percent—are "other character, personality, and behavior disorders," many of them younger clients, the majority of whom have been in a state hospital. About twenty percent are psychoneurotic disorders, the majority of whom probably have not been in a state hospital. Thirteen percent are those with an alcoholism diagnosis, a group not much dealt with in this study, because of our belief that it deserves separate attention.)

For a long period of time, the economic viability of rehabilitation was a principal basis on which support for the program was garnered. Federal vocational rehabilitation interests pointed out that rehabilitation programs paid off "ten to one"—for every dollar invested in rehabilitation, there was an eventual benefit to the general economy of about ten dollars. With the broadening of the program to its present status, there is somewhat less concern, at the federal level at least, about rehabilitation as a "bargain" and somewhat more about rehabilitation as a humane process that helps afflicted individuals to realize a better quality of life.

The change in the federal focus is illustrated by the fact that the word "vocational" was dropped when the name of the agency was changed in 1967 to the Social and Rehabilitation Service in recognition of the need to include services for the disadvantaged and others on welfare, many of whom need social rehabilitation but are not necessarily prospects for vocational training. The goal with mental patients is no longer exclusively one of employment but in given cases may be only to enable them to live in the community rather than in a state hospital.

There have been some moves in this direction among the states. Fifteen have now dropped the term "vocational" from the name of the agency. Traditionally rehabilitation has been attached to the state departments of education, but some of the just-mentioned fifteen states have now established separate rehabilitation commissions or departments.

Many of the states, however, have lagged well behind the federal program, frequently failing to avail themselves of the broadened provisions for support. For example, while there is no stipulation in the federal program about the length of time one must be employed in order to be considered rehabilitated, most states continue to use a thirty-day period. This was viewed by all of the rehabilitation personnel we talked with during this study as grossly inadequate in the case of mental patients. Other states use a ninety-day period for defining "closure," while only about ten use a six-month period. (Theoretically the federal program would permit each state to use a one-year period, although in the light of practical realities, probably no longer.)

Miss Mary Switzer, director of the federal vocational rehabilitation program for many years until early 1970, expressed the movement of philosophy of rehabilitation quite well in a 1964 statement.

> Vocational rehabilitation, like many other aspects of human affairs, has evolved through three stages of public attitudes — compassion without action, followed by willingness to act for economic reasons, followed by willingness to act for social reasons. It seems to me that we are at a transitional state between the last two, with almost universal acceptance of the economic soundness of returning disabled people to employment and a slowly growing philosophy that an advanced civilization like ours should so order its systems that all disabled people will be restored as fully as possible, regardless of any economic benefits to anyone.

IN THE FIRST TWELVE YEARS during which funds were available for research and demonstration programs, a total of 117 such grants were awarded in the "mental and personality disorders" category (plus an additional 17 in the alcoholism category).* These range broadly in subject matter, and include a few grants described as dealing with psychological aspects of the rehabilitation of such special groups as prisoners, plus a few grants to make films. There seem to be about 105 that have to do essentially with demonstration and research relating to rehabilitating people with major mental illness. The number of awards per year has not shown any regular pattern but rather has fluctuated considerably, as follows:

Year	Number of grants	Year	Number of grants
1956	2	1963	12
1957	8	1964	26
1958	7	1965	9
1959	4	1966	10
1960	10	1967	4
1961	14	1968	3
1962	8		

The number of grants awarded according to type of facility receiving them was:

Workshops	22
University departments other than those in schools of medicine	16
State vocational rehabilitation agencies	13
Mental health associations	9
Community-based treating facilities	9
University medical schools	9
State hospitals	8
Psychosocial rehabilitation centers	5
Private psychiatric hospitals	3
Schools	3
Halfway houses	2
Family agencies	2
Other and miscellaneous	16

There were an additional five grants awarded in 1969.

---

*The material that follows is based on *Research and Demonstration Projects,* Social and Rehabilitation Service, Department of Health, Education, and Welfare, Washington, D.C., 1968.

DURING THE LATE 1950's and into the 1960's the National Institute of Mental Health awarded several hundred grants for research and, particularly, demonstration programs, not only in the aspects of rehabilitation with which we are particularly concerned here, but in every aspect of mental health services designed to enable people to leave hospitals and to avoid hospitalization, to have immediate access to service in times of acute disturbance and emergency, and in general to lead useful lives in the community. These included, in addition to community-based residential and workshop facilities and ex-patient social clubs, such services as home treatment, foster home placement, day hospitals, night hospitals, homemaker services, aftercare services, community mental health centers, walk-in clinics, time-limited crisis intervention treatment, consultation programs to schools and other community agencies, suicide prevention programs, family therapy, and general hospital psychiatry. The target population for a great many of the grants were the traditional categories of the mentally ill, while other grants were involved with mental health problems of the general population and of such various special populations as juvenile delinquents, minority groups, the poor, the mentally retarded, and the "marginal normal" population.

The period of greatest research and demonstration activity was the early 1960's. By 1966 almost 500 such grants had been awarded. Among these were approximately fifteen to halfway houses, including Woodley House in Washington, D.C.,* Alpine House in Provo, Utah, and Wellmet in Boston. There were approximately ten grants to ex-patient clubs, such as Friendship Center in Columbia, South Carolina, and the Magnolia Club in New Orleans. A few grants went to sheltered workshops, including notably to ALTRO Workshops in New York City, to the Jewish Vocational Service in Milwaukee, and to the Goodwill Industries workshops in Pueblo, Colorado, and Chicago.

Some demonstrations and a good deal of research continue to be funded since the mid-1960's, but the emphasis has lessened somewhat for at least two reasons. First, the National Institute of Mental Health concluded on the basis of the early demonstrations that the efficacy of such community-based rehabilitation resources for a large number of patients was already demonstrated. A large number of staff from the NIMH central office and regional offices visited the demonstration programs and incorporated their experiences into their own approach to

---

*For a full portrait of this important pioneering program, see N. Rothwell and J. Doniger: *The Psychiatric Halfway House: A Case Study*. Charles C. Thomas, Springfield, Ill., 1966.

program planning and evaluation. Second, with the advent of the community mental health center legislation, the Institute focused its energies more on the development of comprehensive community-based mental health services and less on particular program components.

Of the six psychosocial rehabilitation centers described in this volume, five received NIMH research or demonstration grants, as indicated in the individual program descriptions.

IT WILL BE RECALLED that after the federal program of support to community mental health centers came into being in 1963, regulations were issued that identified five *essential* services* that any program would be required to offer in order to qualify for federal funds to help build a facility or to help meet the costs of staffing one. The regulations also set forth some additional services that must be offered by centers in order to meet the federal definition of *comprehensive*. One of these additional services is rehabilitation. Thus, for some years such rehabilitative components of community mental health centers as halfway houses and sheltered workshops have been eligible to receive federal support.

The regulations permit any community mental health center already in operation and seeking to expand its services to apply for an additional grant to help develop such rehabilitation efforts. However, very few such applications have been received, since most of the new centers have been struggling to recruit the staff and the matching funds to establish the five required services.

In mid-1970 the sharp curtailment of funds to the community mental health center program, together with a backlog of grants already approved for funding, make the availability of funds problematic.

One notable comprehensive rehabilitation center has been built under the community mental health center program, namely, the splendid new physical plant that Horizon House occupies (see p. 100). This program has contracted to provide a complete range of rehabilitation services to two of the community mental health centers in Philadelphia.

---

*These are *a*) inpatient service, *b*) outpatient service, *c*) partial hospitalization service consisting at least of a day care program, *d*) emergency service, and *e*) consultation and education service.

V. The Current Status of Rehabilitation in the Community

W E CAN ATTEMPT TO ASSESS the current status of community-based rehabilitation in two ways: the statistics regarding the numbers of people being served in various kinds of rehabilitation resources, and the outcome studies of research and demonstration programs as reported in the literature. Neither provides as much or as accurate information as one would wish. Statistics, to the extent that they are available at all, began to be collected very recently, so that there are scarcely any comparative figures available. For some types of rehabilitation resources, only the roughest estimates exist.

As for reports of outcome of such rehabilitation efforts as work programs, transitional residences, and social clubs, our literature search disclosed surprisingly few. By and large they are uninformative for one or more of several reasons:

• The number of subjects was too small, in some cases involving no more than five to ten members or clients.

• Either there was no control group, or else there turned out to be such dissimilarities between the control and the experimental groups as to render the control group invalid.

• The study went on over too short a period of time for the outcome data to have meaning.

• There was no follow-up.

Many of the articles in the literature are merely descriptive, with no outcome data. In any case, we have attempted to bring together such information and estimates as exist.

Workshop programs

The National Association of Sheltered Workshops estimates that there are about 1300 workshops in the United States, of which about one thousand are thought to accept people with a mental illness diagnosis. Relatively few of these are exclusively for the mentally ill; much more often it is a matter of intermixing the mentally ill with other kinds of handicapped people.

The Association estimates that on a given day about 60,000 people attend these workshops, but it has no estimate for the proportion that might be mental illness clients. As evidence that the idea of including the mentally ill is still by and large new to sheltered workshops, the Association cites a 1967 Department of Labor survey reporting the various categories of clients served, wherein mental illness was not even one of the category headings. The Association feels that workshops have, all in all, resisted the mentally ill for a variety of reasons, but it seems to see some movement in the recent past toward including them. In any case, it estimates that at most a few thousand mental illness clients are now attending sheltered workshops.

Barton* gives three reasons for the developing interest in sheltered workshops for the mentally ill:

• Some mental patients, even though mentally handicapped, are capable of re-employment, provided work is available under expert supervised guidance.

• The sheltered workshop offers orientation to work, fosters the development of work attitudes as well as specific occupational skills, and provides an opportunity to evaluate the industrial capacity of the particular handicapped individual.

• The stimulus of a real work situation, the acceptance of the individual as he is, regardless of his success or failure, the motivation provided by earning some money, and the example of his fellow handicapped workers do seem to help a significant number (Barton estimates 25 to 30 percent) to become capable of self-support.

POSSIBLY THE LARGEST SINGLE EXPERIMENT with mental patients in sheltered work is that begun at the Brockton, Massachusetts, Veterans Administration Hospital in 1961. Called CHIRP (for "community-hospital-industry rehabilitation program"), it provides a "money incentive" to patients through a diverse program of sheltered work and educational and manual arts therapies. Its aim is to stabilize the patient at his highest functional level, in the community if possible. Training within the hospital and experience in sheltered employment outside are provided in the belief that this will make transition to autonomous community life easier for the patient. About twenty percent of the hospital's patients take part in the program, including schizophrenics, neurotics, and some with chronic brain syndromes. During the first four years 1400

---

*W. E. Barton: *Administration in Psychiatry.* Charles C. Thomas, Springfield, Ill., 1962.

patients went through the program. Twenty-one percent of these had to be readmitted to the hospital. The patient selects his work from a considerable variety of projects. His ability to do the work and the evident benefits from the program are evaluated during an orientation period. Working conditions strongly resemble those of factories on the outside. Just before discharge a patient may still live in the hospital but hold a full-time job in a factory or outside business. The program reports that recruiting a sufficient flow of suitable work from industry requires a great deal of constant effort. The CHIRP program has by this time been implemented in a number of other Veterans Administration hospitals.*

Special mention should be made of the largest network of sheltered workshops, those run by the Goodwill Industries. The first was established in 1902, when Dr. Edgar Helms of Boston picked up old clothes and began to sell them to the poor at low prices. In its early years the Goodwill workshops employed only the crippled, but later included the blind, and eventually a large number of disability categories.

To the best knowledge of Goodwill Industries of America, the national organization of the individual workshops, all 141 now accept people who have a history of mental illness. About one third of the 141 are believed to have full-fledged rehabilitation programs; outstanding examples are those in Cincinnati and Winston-Salem.

Goodwill describes itself as moving away from terminal placements, but states that many of its individual workshops are still serving large numbers of people who evidently must be considered terminal. The New York City program is building a residential facility for such people, partially funded by the Social and Rehabilitation Service.

Traditionally, about 60 to 75 percent of the Goodwill budget of $100,000,000 per year has come from the sale of clothes and various repaired goods, but the percentage is declining. Mr. Matthew Warren, public relations director for the national organization, attributes this to affluence; nobody, not even welfare clients, wants second-hand shoes any more. As this source of funds diminishes, Goodwill anticipates increasing its contract work, which involves packaging, sorting, and so on, in many cases consisting of seasonal overloads from private industry.

In 1969, the Goodwill Industries estimates, its workshops were serving about 24,000 people per day. During that year they restored 7000 people to the competitive labor market. They are unable to estimate what portion are people with a history of mental illness.

---

*For a fuller description of CHIRP, including a step-by-step procedure for those who wish to develop such a program, see W. Winick: *Industry in the Hospital: Mental Rehabilitation Through Work*. Charles C. Thomas, Springfield, Ill., 1967.

Halfway houses

Halfway houses are supervised community residences that provide accommodation and in most cases meals for a variety of disability groups. Those serving the mentally ill began to be established in the 1950's. The greatest period of growth appears to be in the past five years. Most of the halfway houses place a time limit of a few months up to a year on stay (although it is often not very rigidly enforced), since most seem to need to see themselves as transitional facilities designed to bolster up the capability of their residents to move on to some more independent form of living in the community.

Identifying surveys of halfway houses have been carried out both by the Joint Information Service and by the Biometry Branch of the National Institute of Mental Health. At this writing, not all of the data have been analyzed. However, it appears that there are approximately 200 halfway houses serving the mentally ill, plus about an equal number that accept alcoholics only. Among those accepting the mentally ill, almost half also accept other disability categories, such as the mentally retarded, the physically handicapped, alcoholics, drug addicts, and occasionally people released from correctional facilities.

Raush and Raush* in 1963 attempted an identifying survey in which they were able to find only 38 halfway houses serving the mentally ill. Those who pioneered in the halfway house field are thus enthusiastic about the rate at which these facilities are now being established. But there is another side to the coin. Even if all of the approximately two hundred halfway houses that accept mental patients accepted no other kinds of clients, and if each had fifteen beds (many are smaller than this), there would still be, in late 1969, only three thousand people living in halfway houses, as contrasted with between 500,000 and 600,000 who are resident in various psychiatric inpatient facilities.† We believe from what we have read and heard in the course of this project that there are large numbers of inpatients—perhaps as many as 100,000—who might well be able to live in the community, provided there were openings for them in halfway houses. This would indicate the need for several thousand halfway houses, rather than only about two hundred.

---

*H. L. Raush and C. L. Raush: *The Halfway House Movement: A Search for Sanity*. Appleton-Century-Crofts, New York, 1968.

†This figure includes not only those in state hospitals but others in Veterans Administration hospitals, private psychiatric hospitals, psychiatric units of general hospitals, etc.

Ex-patient clubs

Clubs for people who have been mental patients began in the 1940's and for some years grew slowly. Barton† states that the oldest in the United States is probably the one started at a Menninger Clinic building in 1947, followed shortly thereafter by a club at the Massachusetts Mental Health Center. He identifies three principal assumptions upon which the development of ex-patient clubs seems to be based.

• The former patient is not likely to have many friends, and is likely to have great difficulty in making new ones. The social club offers help in developing social relationships, in the belief that the inability to make a satisfactory social adjustment contributes to relapse and rehospitalization.

• The club offers the ex-patient an acceptance that he needs; he can talk there about his mental illness, be accepted as he is, and have allowances made for his need to be dependent or his inability to work.

• The club oftentimes can provide advice or referral when the former patient is in trouble.

Since there is no agency with responsibility for compiling statistics on the number of social clubs and the number of individuals they serve, one must rely on gross estimates. Mabel Palmer, a social worker who has written a volume describing how to organize a social club for ex-patients,* estimates that there were only about forty clubs when she was preparing this volume in the mid-1960's. She believes on the basis of the response to her publication that the number has grown substantially and by 1970 may have passed 150. (These are exclusive of the several hundred Recovery, Inc., groups described below.) Some of these were started under the sponsorship of local mental health associations concerned about the poor sociability prospects for former state hospital patients. A few each were started by state hospitals, community mental health centers, church groups, and such civic organizations as the YMCA. There are no figures at all on how many attend.

The one network of social clubs is Recovery, Inc., organized by Dr. Abraham Low, a Chicago psychiatrist. The meetings, typically held once a week, focus on the writings of Dr. Low, followed by panel presentations of his "Recovery Method," which emphasizes "will training." By

---

†W. E. Barton: *Administration in Psychiatry*. Charles C. Thomas, Springfield, Ill., 1962.

*M. Palmer: *The Social Club: A Bridge from Mental Hospital to Community*. National Association for Mental Health, New York, 1966.

the club's account, it had, in 1963, 1800 dues-paying members in 250 groups in 20 states. The 1970 directory lists 784 groups in 43 states and four Canadian provinces, and 7100 paid members.

Psychosocial rehabilitation centers

Of the "comprehensive" rehabilitation resources which provide some service in all three of the above areas, we have indicated that we were able to locate only a dozen in the entire United States, plus one in Canada. Six of these are the particular subject of the second section of this report.

SIX PROGRAM DESCRIPTIONS

VI. Fountain House
New York

FOUNTAIN HOUSE was the first psychosocial rehabilitation center to be established in the United States. Together with Horizon House in Philadelphia, it is one of the two largest and most nearly comprehensive in program. From its attractive six-story headquarters in mid-Manhattan, it provides an impressive array of socialization, vocational, and residential services to many hundreds of persons with a history of mental illness, in a program that operates every day of the year.

Origins

Fountain House was started by patients on the wards of Rockland State Hospital. During the early 1940's a group of patients met together there to help each other get out of the hospital and to facilitate their community adjustment once they left. They were greatly assisted by a volunteer, Mrs. Howard Schermerhorn, who became the first president of Fountain House. From 1945 onward the discharged patients began to meet in New York City, first occasionally and then regularly, on the steps of the main New York City library, at 42nd Street and Fifth Avenue, later at coffee shops and the YMCA. Calling themselves WANA, an acronym for "We Are Not Alone," the group had no backing and no auspices—professional, political, or financial—other than the support of some volunteers. They came together out of their mutual need for comfort and assurance and their desire to stay in touch with each other. A warm welcome was extended to patients recently discharged from the hospital. Members of the club visited patients still in the hospital in the belief that this might hasten their discharge. They helped each other find jobs and places to live, obtain welfare assistance, and so on. Every effort was made to avoid a clinical or institutional atmosphere. Individual and group therapy, for example, were considered inappropriate.

In mid-1948, through the leadership of two of the volunteers who had become interested in the program, funds were raised to buy a small four-story brownstone on West 47th Street. A board of directors was formed.

41

The name was changed to Fountain House, because of a small and charming fountain located in the patio.

Taking occupancy proved an exciting event for members, volunteers, and the board members. Everyone helped to scrub floors and paint walls. In those early years, the clubhouse provided mainly an evening social program. In the mid-1950's, concurrent with the hiring of the present director, John Beard, a social worker, a daytime program was added to encourage and enhance the vocational potential of the many members who were unemployed and at the same time a "transitional employment" program was begun. Shortly thereafter a program of providing residence in apartments leased by Fountain House was added. Since then, Fountain House has grown steadily in every respect—its base of professional and citizen support, its budget, its facilities, and its program.

Philosophy, purpose, and policies

Fountain House tries to help its members adjust to living in the community by reaffirming in them a sense of belonging and being needed. In the social program it does this by constructing a special community in which all are symbolically members of the same extended family, with new attitudes and values about friendship, feeling accepted, helping one another, and working together. In doing this, staff members do not seem to be concerned about creating dependency on the agency; rather, they acknowledge that many dependency needs are legitimate and positive, in the sense that all of us are dependent on our families, friends, and colleagues.

The Fountain House approach to work and to residential facilities takes a different tack—jobs are real jobs, not placements in sheltered workshops, and living is in apartments throughout the community, not in halfway houses.

A way in which Fountain House contrasts markedly with more traditional kinds of mental health facilities is in its emphasis not solely on verbal relationships but also on nonverbal modes of establishing relationships, by such means as having the staff participate side by side with members in such activities as mopping the floor and preparing lunch.

Fountain House views the process of illness as largely responsible for the isolation and alienation of its members, and sees the illness as the agent that initially brings the member to Fountain House. But it is the strengths and capabilities of the individual that constitute his participation and validate his membership and belonging. For many, the self-awareness that comes at Fountain House of one's own contributions and capabilities is the beginning of the discovery that one is worth something and may well be able to achieve reasonably full participation in the life of the community at large. The impact of Fountain House is largely as an attitude and a climate that pervades its specific program. The attitude/climate has been carefully planned and nurtured over the years. It is intended to convey to the patient that he is accepted and that he belongs. The climate is also conceived of as providing an auxiliary family structure that contains many of the same qualities of mutual concern, learning, role-model identification, discipline, and expectation as might be found in a healthy family.

The director, John Beard, has a well-thought-out rationale for why the people who come to Fountain House have had so poor an outcome with the mental health facilities that have previously served them, the respects in which they are similar to and different from other kinds of handicapped people, and what this means in formulating a program that will serve them adequately.

> The hurt that has been done to the mentally ill in the past is not, in my view, due to the lack of a bed, a place to keep warm, or food to eat. Hostility to mental patients is not avoided simply by feeding and clothing them and keeping them warm. Such care is indeed respectable but it is not sufficient, and all of the methods are still available to reject the patient, to dehabilitate him, and to prevent him from achieving his maximum level of fulfillment and functioning. One can think in terms of interest, of love, or of the human responsibility we have to patients who in past years have become disabled due to our methods of care. The providing of food, clothing, and shelter can still enable the child to feel, if not to say: "Well, what you haven't done is talk with me, get mad at me, fight with me. You've let me do all kinds of things, but you have never really told me how you feel about me and what I am doing and where I'm going." As we know, all too often this has been the way with the mentally ill person in a custodial institution.

Mr. Beard finds it useful to compare the attitudes toward reintegrating the physically handicapped with those about socializing the person with a history of mental illness.

> Everyone seems to accept that we must do something about the man who has no legs — that it is preposterous just to keep saying, "This man cannot walk." If you said this to a good doctor, he would say, "Get with it, let's put this man into an institute of physical rehabilitation, and give him limbs, and teach him to walk on them." Are you then going to say, when you see this man walking on artificial legs, that he's not really walking? Of course he's walking.
>
> A lot of theaters now have ramps so that people in wheel chairs can

go in and laugh and cry and applaud with everyone else. And we say, "Isn't that beautiful? We're really caring about human beings." But there are invisible ramps in the mental health area that are every bit as valid and every bit as useful. Do we fail to create them because this is a way of expressing our rejection of people who are mentally ill?

We took the chains away some time ago, but we didn't go all the way. When we took away certain brutalities, we instituted more subtle rejection devices that were in a sense just as damaging.

At Fountain House we try to go further. It's important, we believe, for people who have a history of mental illness to be needed by the community, not just theoretically, but practically. There should be organizations in every city that want, and therefore reach out for, the schizophrenic patient in the same way that corporations are reaching out for young Ivy League graduates.

Fountain House sees the socially and vocationally disabled schizophrenic as typically requiring a long-term commitment in the hope of compensating for the deficits he is troubled with even when the illness is in remission.

If we took even the very best, most highly recovered member we have ever had at Fountain House and presented him for examination to a psychiatric resident, if that resident were competent he would still make a diagnosis of schizophrenia. But that's not relevant, because the member is functioning in society. The diagnosis becomes just academic. So my persuasion is that the reason schizophrenics in the community are in such bad shape is because we've failed to give them the kinds of experiences that will maximize their ego function. We're not very interested in their pathology, or their childhood, either, but in teaching them what they need to know and giving them the supports they have to have to work and to live in the community and have a decent kind of life.

Fountain House is troubled that among other mental health agencies there is not a greater variation in their approaches to patients. It does not accept that the poor outcome for so many schizophrenics is due simply to a process of illness. Rather, it suspects that professionals in their pattern of care have helped to develop the illness. "Training institutions need to carefully examine the ways in which they prepare professionals who, when in practice, contribute to and perpetuate patterns of care which maintain or develop the disability of the patient."

Fountain House has made several research studies to attempt to ascertain the success of its program in terms of the productivity, income, and so on of its members, but it did not seem to us to view statistical or economic success as a necessary justification for its efforts.

Fountain House completed one of the first experimental studies using control groups to determine whether or not the program influenced rehospitalization rates. It has recently received a five-year Social and Rehabilitation Service grant to conduct a series of evaluative studies. But in the meantime it feels itself obligated to provide to its members a social environment based upon humanistic values even if effectiveness is not yet demonstrated.

Julius Lanoil, a sociologist who is the Fountain House program director, aptly describes the program as "a kind of moral therapy. We don't believe in 'doing your own thing' if your own thing happens to be yelling, stealing, or cursing. Fountain House has a value system that it attempts to impart, in the same way that healthy parents do. The healthy family should be the greatest type of therapeutic community, and we have tried to institutionalize that kind of influence and basic values."

Dr. Saul Fisher, one of three psychiatrists who spend six hours a week each at Fountain House, feels it important for psychiatric participation to be limited. "Extensive psychiatric involvement has the potential of turning the program into a clinic, at the risk of losing its rehabilitation focus," he told us. "If the goal is integrating the patient into the community, then the services have to be community-oriented."

As yet, Fountain House has not entered into any formal relationships with any of the five community mental health centers now operating in New York City, although many of its members are in treatment at one of the centers. Because of its large capacity, it may in time serve several centers. Fountain House feels that one of its important contributions is to serve as prototype, in the hope that its successes will be heeded by community-based mental health services which will then develop their own rehabilitation programs.

Management and administration

The managerial and administrative aspects of Fountain House are elusive, and several of the staff suggested that this was because of the emphasis on operating the agency as a therapeutic community.

The agency continued until the recent past to operate and grow by maintaining a fairly consistent pattern of "simple expansion." Ultimately it became so large both in program, staff, and number of members that this was no longer possible.

Consequently two changes were made: *a*) an administrator was added to the staff, to take over many of the day-to-day problems that had been the responsibility of the director; and *b*) the program was divided into five units, each taking responsibility for all aspects of the member's rehabilitation.

Each unit is intended to become essentially autonomous—"a little Fountain House"—doing its own intakes, scheduling its own activities, making its own referrals for employment and to community agencies, following up dropouts, overseeing its own day program activities, transitional employment, and apartment placements.

The unitization was undertaken because of the feeling that the staff should be highly visible and well known not only to all their members but to each other as well, in the interest of facilitating interactions and developing close working relationships. The corollary to this is the philosophy that staff should not be so highly specialized that they cannot empathize and communicate with fellow staff members.

We asked a social worker to describe the chain of command, and he responded that he had "never given any thought to a chain of command." But when it was suggested to him that the agency "hangs loose," he responded:

> On the contrary I would say that it "hangs tight"; that is, very little happens around here that we don't all learn about very quickly.

When we asked him to whom he would turn for advice, consultation, or authorization in several different sorts of problems, in each case he named a different member of the senior staff.

There are at Fountain House a director, an assistant director, an administrator, a program director, a program coordinator, and various others who might ordinarily be viewed as "the establishment." But the division of labor appears to have been arrived at consensually, struggle for authority seems to be absent, and the sense of comfort about relationships within the staff seems remarkably good. In terms of day-to-day operations, the hierarchy at Fountain House appears to be as flat as possible for an agency of its size.

In terms of requirements imposed by official agencies, Fountain House must abide by the regulations of the New York City Department of Mental Health and Mental Retardation in order to receive matching funds from them. Its premises must pass inspection by the fire department. The state department of social welfare imposes certain regulations concerning charitable nonprofit organizations. A "certificate of occupancy" limits capacity to a maximum of 535 persons at a time. And the thrift shop must meet certain standards imposed by the city. Fountain House is exempt from federal taxes.

Physical facilities

Fountain House is now located across the street from the original small brownstone on 47th Street. Located a few blocks from Times Square, and readily accessible by public transportation from all parts of New York City, the new building was built especially for Fountain House, at a cost of approximately $2,000,000, which came principally from philanthropy, with about $400,000 in Hill-Burton funds.

The six-story building, with more than 30,000 square feet of space, is located on a middle- to lower-middle-class street of apartment buildings and brownstones that have been converted into apartments. The building was designed to give the appearance of a spacious private home, and the furnishings have been well selected to maintain a homelike atmosphere. The rooms are large and have high ceilings. The decor might be characterized as "contemporary colonial," with restful color schemes, furniture in rich woods, and attractive chandeliers.

On the main floor, just off a spacious center-hall entrance, are a reception room, an interviewing room, and a large living room. The first floor also contains a television lounge, a photography dark room, a large area for table games, some office space for the transitional employment program, and the membership office, where members can check their coats and pick up their mail.

The second floor contains a music room, a library, a small lounge, a large terrace with flower beds and a fountain, and the administrative offices. The third floor contains a beauty shop and a sewing room, three rooms used for individual interviews, and two large offices for program staff (most staff workers do not have their own offices). The fourth floor houses a large clerical training area, a classroom, and a room for art activities. The fifth floor has an attractive snack bar and a roof garden. The basement consists of a large kitchen and a large dining room where lunch is served to more than 300 members each day. Immediately adjoining the dining room is an auditorium with a well-equipped stage.

When Fountain House opens for the day at 9:00 a.m., the large house seems empty but becomes progressively more busy as members come in. By noontime it is a beehive of activity. The pace eases off again in the afternoon, to pick up once more in the late afternoon as members start coming in for the evening program.

Fountain House is one of the most attractive mental health facilities that any of the authors have seen. It is interesting that although the furnishings seem almost opulent they have remained in excellent condition despite constant use.

Fountain House recently acquired the brownstone next door and is in the process of renovating it into a research center, which will include a great deal of audio-visual equipment to be used in developing materials for training and member orientation.

Around the corner from Fountain House is a thrift shop which the agency rents. It is an ordinary and somewhat dilapidated store. In 1969 it realized an income of $25,000 as well as providing many opportunities for members to perform in roles that bring them into direct contact with the community.

The staff

Of 56 full-time and ten part-time staff members at Fountain House, only the three part-time psychiatric consultants appear to have responsibilities that significantly draw on the content of their training and fall within the traditional role of their particular profession. These men act principally as clinical rather than program consultants. They handle emergencies among members; they prescribe medication when a member needs an emergency supply or for the occasional member who has not established a medication source with one of the clinics or community mental health centers; they provide psychiatric evaluations of persons who are applying for Division of Vocational Rehabilitation sponsorship and for members seeking drivers' licenses.

The rest of the staff can be divided roughly into two categories: a) those who are untrained in any of the mental health disciplines and have learned what they need to know after they came to the job; and b) those who have been trained in any of several mental health disciplines, notably social work and rehabilitation counseling, who came directly to Fountain House from training and then had to learn on the job what was lacking in their training, or else came to Fountain House from some more traditional setting in which they were dissatisfied. This may to some extent oversimplify, but by and large it seems to account for the majority of the bright, energetic, and enthusiastic staff.

We asked Mr. Beard how he predicts whether an applicant for a Fountain House job will be suitable. He replied that over the years he has not been able to develop useful criteria. For the most part it appears to be a matter of trial and error, "although it doesn't take a great deal of time." If after about three months the new staff person has not begun to grasp the rationale and catch the spirit of Fountain House, he is helped to realize that he will probably be better off in a more traditional agency.

Some of the staff have applied to Fountain House because of their prior knowledge of the program, in a few cases through a placement there during training, sometimes because they have worked in an agency that referred clients to Fountain House, and sometimes simply by its general reputation. Mr. Beard explained the attraction that Fountain House has held in this way:

> People want to feel significant, and to do so they must get into a setting whose purpose is conducive to feeling significant. Because we are working with clients who are "the least promising," our staff feel that any success or accomplishment is significant. Take our restaurant project. We have very sick, vocationally disabled members there, 17 of them, and they are working, earning real salaries, in a real place of business that is making a profit. The staff can respond to this kind of success. Of course, they are testing all the time, because they don't want to be caught up in phony situations, nor to feel exploited or misled.

There is an ambivalence at Fountain House about formal training. Some of their most valuable, and indeed charismatic, staff members have only a high school education. Some of the products of highly reputed training facilities have been unable to accept the untraditional ways of Fountain House, where social workers have no desk of their own, where interviews with members are conducted in the course of preparing lunch, cleaning the common rooms, or sorting clothes for the thrift shop. Fountain House emphasized to us repeatedly that it has nothing *against* the professionally trained person, and from having such people on the staff gains fundable positions and an air of respectability for the benefit of fellow agencies. But it also emphasized that training in itself does not assure that a person will be able to relate in the personal and involved manner that characterizes the services of Fountain House—indeed, that the training may be antithetical. It is important to note that while the pay scale is equated with professional credentials, there is also provision for exceptional performance by persons with no previous training, so that untrained staff may in some cases be paid more than some who have graduate degrees.

Starting in the recent past all new staff members have been assigned to the kitchen to help prepare lunch along with approximately sixty of the members and a remarkable untrained staff member, Mrs. Esther Kruuse, who has risen to the position of assistant program director. This locus was chosen for orienting new staff members precisely because of the exceptional qualifications of Mrs. Kruuse for working with the members. Warm, empathic, and highly demanding, she has been known to plead—successfully—with a member who had announced his intention of returning to the hospital.

On the face of it the structure of the staff is not difficult to understand; there are "senior staff," consisting mostly of persons with formal training, who are assigned particular components of the agency's operation, such as program director and program coordinator; and the junior staff who are assigned to the five units described above. The lines of reporting are, however, difficult to understand, and one is hard put to know what induces a junior staff member in a given case to take his problem to some particular senior staff member rather than some other.

Ordinarily one might anticipate that such a situation would result in misunderstanding, frustration, and confusion, but it seems not to. While communications seem to be implemented in an informal, unstructured way, the seeming absence of formal channels clearly does not bother the staff or lessen their sense of fitting into the agency. The staff at all levels seem well integrated into the stream of activities and developments. If they suffer from any sense of dislocation, they do not show it. Although there are brief daily unit meetings, there are almost never full-staff meetings. People who need to communicate with anyone other than the members of their own units hold their conferences and make their decisions as they pass each other in the hall, take coffee breaks, or meet at a nearby tavern for a drink after working hours.

Volunteers

Approximately twenty volunteers participate in the evening and weekend recreational programs. Those with specific skills in photography, dramatics, and music lead such activities. Volunteers also participate in the apartment program by helping members clean and decorate their quarters. Volunteers have also often helped to locate jobs for the transitional employment program.

Fountain House has not actively recruited volunteers in the recent past, but through community contacts has developed a small corps who participate regularly. Applicants are interviewed and, if accepted, attend three orientation sessions. They are then screened by one of the psychiatric consultants prior to assignment.

The clientele

Eligibility and referral sources. Any person with a history of mental illness is eligible to become a member of Fountain House except those with a primary diagnosis of alcoholism or drug addiction and those who have a history of criminal antisocial behavior. Other factors may preclude participation, for example uncontrolled epilepsy or aggressive homosexual behavior. Self-referrals are accepted, provided the applicant has some medical backup or some other source from which background information can be obtained. The vast majority of Fountain House members have been hospitalized once, or numerous times, in the state hospitals of New York. For some years the principal source of members was the state hospitals, but more recently it has shifted to the aftercare clinics operated by the New York State Department of Mental Hygiene. Thereafter, in descending order of frequency, the sources of referral are state hospitals, private hospitals, outpatient clinics, the state Division of Vocational Rehabilitation, psychiatrists in private practice, and a few from a variety of other agencies.

Characteristics of the clients. Membership at Fountain House is not limited to a specific time. A member is terminated or placed on inactive status whenever he fails to attend the program at least once during a three-month period. Presently some 1000 men and women use the facility in the course of three months. Close to 1000 applications are received each year. Over eighty percent have a diagnosis of schizophrenia. Some sixty percent of applicants are male. Almost one half of all applicants are in the age range of 25 to 40; another 25 percent are from 17 to 25, and the remaining 25 percent are from 40 to 78. Four out of five applicants are unemployed at intake, receiving financial assistance from public welfare, social security disability, veteran benefits, or support from their families. Three out of four applicants seek membership within four months of leaving the hospital. Almost half reside in Manhattan, most of the balance living in Brooklyn and the Bronx. Almost three out of four are single and most of those who were ever married are no longer. At intake almost all applicants are on some form of medication and in contact with an aftercare clinic or other type of medical facility. The proportion of white persons to Negroes approximates their representation in the metropolitan area. While one out of three has not completed high school, almost one out of three has had some college training.

Enrolling and retaining the members

Compared to many mental health facilities, intake at Fountain House is quite simple. At the time of initial contact, either by the prospective member himself or by a referring agency, an intake appointment is scheduled, usually within one or not more than two weeks.

Until recently intake was centralized, with the intake staff consisting of a senior mental health professional and two nonprofessionals who were trained at Fountain House. For a variety of reasons the intake is in process of being decentralized to the five program units. For one thing, a number of new members became attached to the intake workers and resisted transfer to a program unit. For another, a number did not seem able to make an immediate commitment to a nine-to-four work program and instead simply lounged around for a time before accepting assignment to a unit.

Under both the old and the new procedures, the applicant is met at the door by a receptionist who has a list of referrals and the names of the staff members to whom they are assigned. The particular staff member gives the applicant an application form to fill out, and upon completing it he is considered to have become a member of Fountain House. The selection of a particular unit to handle a given applicant's intake is determined partly by such information as is available about his interests, partly by the staff's appraisal of him, partly by the need to balance case-flow among the respective units.

Under this new procedure, each new member is presented at one of the twice-weekly meetings of senior staff of the five units. The intake worker for the unit of initial assignment either indicates her unit's desire to keep the member or to transfer him to another unit that seems more appropriate to his needs, interests, and capabilities.

Audio-visual aids are being prepared which will serve to acquaint each new member with the scope of the entire program, including, for example, the information that there are 40 different employers who offer transitional work, and that 150 patients go to work each day on these assignments and earn a total of $300,000 a year.

Once involved in a unit, the member progresses to a large extent at his own pace, although he is encouraged to perform one or more of the assignments supervised by his unit.

"No-shows." Approximately two thirds of referrals made to Fountain House keep their intake appointments. Those who do not show up are not contacted.

Dropouts. The longer the member participates in the program, the stronger is the staff's investment in him. Consequently, relatively little reaching out is done to those who drop out of the program within the first week or two. Those who have been in the program longer and then drop out are contacted by telephone call, letter, or even a home visit. While motivation is not stressed as a precondition for membership, obviously it must be a factor in the member's getting through the first few weeks, and those who do not have considerable motivation seem unlikely to stay in the program.

The program, in general

More than 300 persons participate each day in the daytime activities of Fountain House, and almost twice that number come in for the evening and weekend programs. The daytime participaiion is expected to exceed 400 by the end of 1970. These figures represent a total of about one thousand different individuals during any given three-month period. The people move in and out of the program, and the caseload is not easy to define because it varies so much from week to week and even from day to day.

None of the elements of the program are compulsory. New members are urged to participate in one of the five daytime units, but those not able to make such a commitment are invited to attend informally and participate in recreational and social activities, or merely to relax, in the hope thereby that they will later become interested in a regular assignment.

There are no written rules about membership at Fountain House. Each new member is given a small brochure that explains the purposes and services of the agency. There are no officers, member government, or house committee; individual members exert their influence within the particular work or social groups in which they participate.

Only occasionally is it necessary to discipline or terminate a member. These instances result usually from grossly unsocial behavior, such as an assault on a fellow member. Once in a while a member is terminated because he has been attending for a long time, has not participated in any of the programmed events, and appears to be gaining no benefit at all from his membership.

The social program

An opportunity for informal free-time socializing, including watching television, listening to music, and playing a variety of games, is provided in the daytime vocational program. Many members spend a portion of the day chatting with each other in the snack bar. Many members who are working drop in at lunch time to relax, chat, or participate in some recreation.

Programmed social activities are concentrated in the evening and weekend program, which includes photography, swimming, dramatics, basketball, and singing groups, trips to the movies, group discussions, weekly dances, and outings to nearby points of interest. The midweek evening program emphasizes the club groups, the Saturday evening program the music, dances, and parties. Sunday is a quiet time when members read the paper, play bingo or cards, and watch television or a movie.

The evening and weekend program is considered especially helpful to members who have full-time jobs. Over the years almost all of the staff have worked at least one evening per week, and this will intensify as the unitization takes full effect, so that each of the unit staff will have some stipulated evening responsibilities, thereby providing continuity of relationship with their daytime members who have moved on to employment.

The vocational program

Perhaps the most impressive aspect of the impressive Fountain House program is its activities in preparing patients for work and finding jobs for them. This can be viewed in two phases: *a*) prevocational activities carried out within the Fountain House setting, and *b*) transitional placements in a large number of businesses and stores.

The prevocational program is the center of all the daytime activities at Fountain House. Substantially all of the members who come there during the day are assigned to one of the prevocational units: the snack bar, the clerical unit, the thrift shop unit, the education and research unit, the kitchen and dining room unit, the reception and intake unit, and the house-cleaning and maintenance unit. These vary considerably in size both in staff and members, with from four to ten staff assigned to a unit, and from 30 to 100 members.

The effect is to convey to the member at least three sentiments: *a*) that there is a great deal of work to be done at Fountain House, *b*) that members are expected to contribute their time and effort, and *c*) that Fountain House needs the members and could not operate without them. Motivation of members is accomplished principally through "role-model education," demonstrated and reinforced by staff and other members, on a seemingly casual basis. If a member seems reticent about participating, he is told, "Try it out, see if you like it." The staff anticipates that his resistance will diminish as he learns to feel comfortable and accepted within his unit program and as he observes the positive attitudes and performances of the other members.

The role of staff in developing and maintaining this spirit is noteworthy. Fountain House strongly believes that the best way to help a client accept responsibility is for a staff member to work side by side with him. This is the respect in which the agency has been most unconventional in the roles and job assignments of its staff. The staff must relate by doing and by sharing with members, for the purpose of creating a special feeling of community, the binding agent of which is member-staff relations built on mutual activities leading in turn to mutual acceptance.

Members typically participate in the work of their assigned unit for about half of the nine-to-four day, spending the rest of their time in unprogrammed recreation and relaxation.

When at a meeting of the unit staff it is decided that a particular member is ready to try employment, he is considered for one of approximately 150 "transitional" jobs available to Fountain House, with a variety of small, independent businesses, as well as with such major firms as Sears, Roebuck, Benton & Bowles, Young & Rubicam, several of the largest banks, and *Newsweek* magazine. The number of jobs per employer ranges from a low of one to a high of ten. Most of the jobs are unskilled, such as messenger, kitchen helper, and mail clerk. Ordinarily a staff member of Fountain House spends a day or two learning any new job. Next, a member is told about the job and encouraged to try it. Often the staff member accompanies the member to the job, and sometimes stays with him for a day or two while he settles in.

While most of the jobs are full time, they are divided into two parts, so that each member works only half a day. Members in the transitional employment program are ordinarily expected to spend the other half day at Fountain House.

The jobs are scheduled on three- to four-month rotations, after which, if a particular member seems to need more work habituation and experience, he can be assigned to another opening. He may not repeat the same placement or return to it later.

Members are paid regular salaries, ranging from $1.60 to $2.25 per hour, and nothing is deducted from this for any form of service.

Fountain House reports that employers are enthusiastic about the program and that the principal source of new jobs has been word-of-mouth from existing placements. The employers rarely hire the transitional employees into their firms, and on the occasions when they have attempted to do so Fountain House has discouraged it on the grounds that the jobs are needed on a rotating basis. Furthermore, Fountain House does not feel it advisable for a member to become a regular employee at a firm where he has had a rehabilitation relationship, and in the few instances where this has occurred it has never worked out.

Some of the jobs are group placements; for example, ten persons as mail clerks, porters, and order takers at Sears, Roebuck, together with a Fountain House staff member who functions as a mental health worker. Her salary is paid by Sears. The group placement seems to provide an important advantage for certain members, since it seems to allow them in entering the employment market to spread their anxiety across the group. The relationship one already holds with the group can substitute for having to make new relationships at a time of stress when everything else is new; and the group can stimulate motivation to work hard and to succeed.

Another group placement that accommodates a number of members is at a particular store of the Chock Full O'Nuts restaurant chain. There seventeen Fountain House members hold down the equivalent of eight full-time jobs. The owner of the franchise for this particular store pays Fountain House $200 per week for the services of a staff member who works at the store as manager. In 1969 a total of sixty Fountain House members spent some time in this transitional employment setting and earned a total of $33,000. The snack bar at Fountain House serves as training ground for this particular placement.

We interviewed the man who owned the Chock Full O'Nuts franchise at the time it first began to take Fountain House members as employees. He had known of Fountain House through a previous business, a commercial stationery house, where he employed two members as delivery boys. After he acquired the Chock Full O'Nuts franchise, he suggested that Fountain House might try placing a member there. He told us:

> We started with one person, part time, and we were pretty apprehensive in the beginning, because waiting on the public was a good deal different from the messenger work. I waited for some outburst, but there wasn't any so within a month we had three people working there. Fountain House and I got more and more involved with each other, and by the time I sold the place all but three of the employees were Fountain House members, and we had had a total of 95 working there. One man who came in looking ashen his first day and couldn't look me in the eye is now the assistant manager.

Fountain House is justifiably proud of the fact that its members earned an aggregate of $300,000 in the transitional employment program last year. The reasons for this success are quite clearly the operating policies of the program. One of the most significant of these is that when an employer commits a job placement to Fountain House, Fountain House promises that the job will be done. This means that when a member does not show up for work, a substitute member must be recruited, and if this is not possible, a Fountain House staff member must go to the job and substitute. Thus the employer is guaranteed that the work will be done. We know of no other vocational program that makes this kind of commitment and gives this kind of service to employers. In this respect, Fountain House does not hesitate to relieve a member of a job that he seems unable to perform; but in practice this rarely happens. The turnover rate of the members is no greater than what an employer might encounter with regular employees.

A LARGE PERCENTAGE OF MEMBERS who participate in the transitional employment service complete more than one thirteen-week assignment. When a member appears to be ready to seek regular employment, Fountain House refers him to the special services desk for handicapped people at the New York State Employment Service. We interviewed the counselor who deals particularly with Fountain House members. Over the years the proportion of mentally handicapped has risen in her work—from about 20 percent seven years ago to about 55 percent at the present time. Many of these are Fountain House members.

While she used to have great difficulty recruiting employers who would accept ex-mental patients as employees, she now receives acceptance from about seventy percent. She does not use any special group of employers because she does not want "to build a ghetto of handicapped people in particular businesses." Rather, she attempts to place her clients in as dispersed a pattern as possible.

Most applicants prefer that the employer know they have been mentally ill, because they know it does not make sense to have large work gaps in their histories. An occasional client requests that the employer not be told. Such persons are more likely to fail in employment, the counselor believes, because the employer does not have the information he needs to shield them from stress.

In a follow-up study of Fountain House referrals she found that a month after placement about fifty percent were still on the assigned job; this contrasts with a seventy percent rate for the physically handicapped. A three-month follow-up showed very little drop from the fifty percent figure. She reports that the outcome with Fountain House referrals who have participated in the transitional employment program is considerably better than with referrals directly from state hospitals.

The residential program

Consistent with its philosophy of not wanting an "institutional" flavor to its program, Fountain House, rather than operate a halfway house, holds the lease on about 25 apartments throughout New York City where slightly more than 50 Fountain House members live. In this way Fountain House minimizes the member's dependency on the agency and at the same time strengthens his concept of himself as being able to live independently in the community. Fountain House holds the lease and pays the rent; it then subleases to two and sometimes three members and collects the rent from them, which they pay mainly with funds from the welfare department and their earnings in Fountain House transitional jobs. In a number of cases roommates who have got along well together have then taken over the lease after a period of time. More often the apartments are used on a rotating basis, since a number of the members prefer to go out and find their own places when they are equipped to undertake leases of their own.

The program has the advantage for members of protecting them from slumlords. Fountain House staff find "open market" apartments that are the best available at their price range, whereas the members, left to their own devices and unsure of themselves, tend to be pushed into small dilapidated rooms at unreasonably high prices. The program also has advantages for the landlord, who is assured that the rent will always be paid, and on time. Often Fountain House staff, volunteers, and members have helped to fix up the apartments. Fountain House assures the landlord that it will provide immediate intervention in the event of trouble, which rarely occurs.

All of the apartments have an extra bed which can be and often is used temporarily for someone just entering the Fountain House program. These are typically people on "trial visit" status from the state mental hospitals.

We visited two of the apartments. One, a fourth-floor "walk up" in a somewhat dilapidated building, was adequate. It had a small bed-sitting room, a good-sized kitchen, and a fairly modern bath. The other, in a renovated building, had a living room, bedroom, kitchen, and bath, and was of quite good quality.

Medication

More than eighty percent of Fountain House members are on psychotropic medication at the time they enter the program. Medication is viewed as extremely important, as evidenced by Mr. Beard's statement that, given a forced choice between medication alone and the Fountain House program alone, he would choose medication.

Members obtain medications for the most part from the New York State aftercare clinics, and in some cases from community mental health centers, other types of outpatient services, and private psychiatrists.

Fountain House feels that many of its members "do not get good psychiatric care, as our psychiatric consultants can document; they're always handling emergencies," many of which have to do with medication problems.

Families

Fountain House describes its interaction with the families of members as minimal. This is in part because many of the members do not have families accessible to them, or because the family relationships are seen as deleterious to the patient.

Agency and community relationships

Fountain House seems to be well known and well regarded within its particular orbit, but, predictably, little known to the public at large. That it has considerable private support is evidenced by the fact that something more than half of its budget is represented by private donations. The agencies that refer to Fountain House and receive referrals from it appear to have a high opinion both of the way it is operated and the quality of its service.

The representative of the state employment service told us that

> they've improved themselves greatly over the years, and they always seem to understand when anything is going wrong. My referral reports come in complete, and there's always someone to discuss the case with. There isn't a problem that comes up that we can't easily solve. It's a pleasure to work with them.

The representative of the New York City Department of Mental Health and Mental Retardation, one of the sources of funds for Fountain House, also spoke highly of the relationship between the two agencies.

Fountain House is located in a particularly anonymous neighborhood and has, as is typical of residents of New York, scarcely any dealings with its neighbors. It has also had no trouble with them.

Training

It was astonishing to learn that, from all the many training institutions in New York City, there were at Fountain House at the time of our visit only four students—one social work student each from Fordham and New York Universities and two vocational counseling students from Columbia Teachers College.

Among the various psychiatric residency programs in New York, only two have placed residents. The principal one is Columbia, and this is attributed largely to the interest and sympathy of the department chairman, Dr. Lawrence Kolb, who has been a member of the Fountain House board for a number of years. Over several years about fifteen psychiatric residents have been assigned to Fountain House for three- to nine-month periods with the intensity of their participation ranging from a half day to three full days per week. Some residents have also come from the New York School of Psychiatry.

The authors could not help feeling that this low utilization of a well-known, well-established, well-reputed rehabilitation facility, virtually the only one devoted exclusively to the mentally ill in a city with numerous training programs, is eloquent testimony to the need for an updating of the content of mental health training.

Finances

Fountain House operates on a current budget of about $800,000, derived from a variety of private and public sources. For 1969, the latest final figures available, the income was $777,000, which came from the following sources:

Contributions by individuals	$ 75,000
Contributions by board members	35,000
Foundation grants and other grants	220,000
Benefits	36,000
New York City Department of Mental Health and Mental Retardation	257,000
State and federal Vocational Rehabilitation	76,000
Thrift shop	23,000
Interest and dividends	44,000
Other	11,000

For the same year expenses were about $766,000, so that Fountain House realized a small excess of income over expenses, a rare occurrence among mental health facilities.

Of $766,000 spent in 1969, $516,000 was for salaries to maintain program and operations. Forty-three thousand dollars was spent for fund raising and public relations, and the balance for a large variety of expenses in program, operations, education, training, and research.

As we have mentioned, Fountain House feels it is crucially important for a substantial portion of its operating funds to come from private sources, and in each year to date it has been successful in deriving more than half of its budget from the private area.

The New York City Department of Mental Health and Mental Retardation makes a block grant to help support what is considered to

be a daytime, evening, and nighttime (the apartment program) rehabilitation service. The funds are matched on a fifty-fifty formula. In
reality, since Fountain House has private funds that can be matched, the
city money is merely a channeling downward of state grant-in-aid; the
limited city funds are reserved to match state money for such poverty
areas as Harlem and Bedford-Stuyvesant, where no private funds are
available for matching.

A limited amount of fee-for-service money—$44,000 in 1969—
comes from the state Division of Vocational Rehabilitation for the
purchase of Personal Adjustment Training services for about 35 Fountain House members. This small program is growing in size, and a DVR
counselor for this group now spends one day a week at Fountain House.
Limited funds are also made available from the state in exchange for
services provided to about twenty deaf psychotic patients placed at
Fountain House by Rockland State Hospital.

None of Fountain House income comes from members. From the
outset there has been a philosophical position against charging any fees
or dues, on the grounds that Fountain House wants to create the most
welcoming climate it possibly can and thus does not want to assess the
member even a nominal amount for the service he receives. This viewpoint is sharply at variance with that of many traditional mental health
facilities, which have placed great emphasis on "the motivational value"
of fees. In increasing numbers Fountain House members have come to
be contributors after they begin working.

Outcome

Fountain House believes that the best available indexes of improvement are *a*) being out of the hospital and *b*) holding a job. Fountain
House would like to be able to measure "enrichment of living" but
believes that the difficulties and complications are so numerous as to
make this almost impossible.

Two studies of outcome have been undertaken over the years, the first
under the auspices of the National Institute of Mental Health, the second
with funds from the Social and Rehabilitation Service. Both studies indicated that ex-hospitalized patients who participate in the Fountain House
program do better in terms of staying out of the hospital and working
than do nonparticipants. It was also clear that patients in the experimental group who went through the transitional employment program
did better with respect to rehospitalization rate than those who did not.
The rate of reduction in rehospitalization—thirty to forty percent—was
virtually identical in the two studies done six years apart. Among the

group assigned to the Fountain House program, those who came for five or fewer visits had a much higher relapse rate than those who attended a greater number of times. Those members who were able to go to work had a much lower relapse rate than those who were completely unable ever to become employed.

Fountain House does not view the findings as definitive, however, because of the short time span imposed on the SRS-funded study. Proposed for a 24-month period, it was cut back to 18. Fountain House believes that such a study, if it is to indicate convincingly the extent to which a community rehabilitation service is successful, must be carried on for a longer period of time, ideally from three to five years. (Since the time of our visit Fountain House has been awarded a five-year research grant by the SRS.)

From a more circumstantial viewpoint, the usefulness of Fountain House can be tentatively documented by the fact that its members placed in transitional employment earn more than $300,000 per year and that a number go on to and succeed in competitive employment. These people are not costing the state of New York approximately $3500 per year each to maintain in mental hospitals, and their earnings serve to reduce the payments they receive from the welfare department. A cost-effectiveness comparison of Fountain House with other methods of maintaining those with a history of mental illness would be extremely useful. We expect that the Fountain House model would turn out to be by far the least expensive.

Plans for the future

Fountain House appears to be more interested at the present in consolidating and intensifying its new organizational format than in expanding its activities. Although Fountain House seems somewhat puzzled and disappointed that the considerable exposure it has had—the agency receives more than one thousand visitors a year—has not led to a greater proliferation of comprehensive, community-based rehabilitation services, at the same time it does not seem to have any plans or desires to create and operate additional Fountain Houses. It seems probable that if funding sources were to approach Fountain House requesting that it establish, for example, additional Fountain Houses for each of the boroughs of New York, it would decline to do so on the grounds that such agencies ought to operate autonomously.

Among the desires for additional program components and for improvement that were expressed to us by various staff members were the following:

•To acquire a property in the country that members and staff members could use on weekends and for retreats and vacations. (Since our visit Fountain House has been given two country properties, a 500-acre tract in Northern New Jersey and a 13-acre estate in New York containing a Huguenot house built in 1760. Both are within two hours' driving time from New York.)

• To strengthen the process of receiving new members, so that, with more intensive intake service, the proportion that make a definite commitment might be increased.

• To start "Fountain House clubs" in certain hospitals that now refer prospective members, so that patients could learn more about Fountain House prior to discharge.

• To increase the proportion of Puerto Rican members, who have not been proportional to their numbers in the population of New York City. (There has been an increase in the recent past, perhaps because several Spanish-speaking staff members have been added.)

VII. Council House
Pittsburgh

COUNCIL HOUSE is a sophisticated and well-staffed facility unique among these six psychosocial rehabilitation centers in that it does not have a physical plant of its own but instead relies on the use of a variety of community facilities. It began modestly in 1957 as a one-night-a-week ex-patient social club sponsored as a service project of the local chapter of the National Council of Jewish Women. Mrs. Anne Schwartz, a social worker who was an organizer of Council House, provided a résumé of how the agency came to be established.

> Our original planning committee was composed of a lawyer, a psychologist, and four social workers. The need for some kind of program for posthospital mental patients seemed apparent. I was particularly inspired by what I had heard about Fountain House, and while I was in New York on a trip I visited them and gathered some material.

> Various of us from the planning committee met with a number of professional and citizens groups in the mental health field. We outlined our plans to establish a "resocialization program" that would serve as a bridge to the community for people who had been in mental hospitals, planning to staff the program entirely with volunteers from the Council of Jewish Women.

> Our proposal did not find a favorable response. The professionals all felt that such a program was greatly needed, and none of them had any plans to start one, but they discouraged us "because volunteers simply cannot run and effectively manage and staff a program of this kind." They raised questions about confidentiality, about whether volunteers would have the skills required to deal with recently discharged psychiatric patients. A notable exception was Dr. Regis Downey of Mayview State Hospital, who felt the idea was worthwhile and offered to cooperate fully with us.

> With a grant of $200 from a member of the Council of Jewish Women we went ahead with our plans to establish Council House. We were convinced from the beginning that meetings should be held downtown, in a location easily accessible from all points of the city. But our "search

teams" were absolutely unsuccessful; the only agency offering space was the Salvation Army, and then only if we enforced their rule against smoking. We ruled this out as creating too much stress for the patients and possibly the volunteers as well.

And so we decided to hold our meetings in the lounge of the Council of Jewish Women. We recruited volunteers through the Council and met with them to prepare for our first meeting. We did not know what to expect, and we all arrived at the first meeting, in April 1957, full of apprehension. The few "members" were mainly discharged patients from Mayview State Hospital. Those first few meetings consisted of card games, playing of records, talking, singing, and light entertainment. They were not a howling success. We never had more than ten or twelve members, and sometimes as few as four or five. The room was too large for so small a group, the location was inconvenient. Then came a long streetcar strike that forced a temporary closing of the program. We reopened late in 1957 in the headquarters of the Pittsburgh Hearing Society downtown and met weekly thereafter.

To publicize the program we arranged for Council House volunteers to sponsor a monthly tea at Mayview State Hospital. But after about six months it was apparent that the people referred on discharge by the hospital were not those we were seeing at our teas. So we then arranged for the hospital to send a busload of patients once a month to our meetings. We also arranged with the Veterans Administration hospital at about that time to involve their patients in our program.

During the first year we began to take members on trips to flower shows, ball games, the civic light opera, the airport, picnics, and sightseeing. At regular meetings the main activity was talking, with card games and some arts and crafts. The volunteers and the patients jointly served the refreshments and cleaned up afterwards, and I recall that to motivate members I washed more dishes at Council House than I ever did at home.

Our major problem in those early days was reassuring the volunteers and their husbands. We had to drop some volunteers whose families were too upset about their dealing with mental patients. Others dropped out when they realized that such a program was not as glamorous as they had anticipated. They found the members dull and unstimulating; no amount of previous training had prepared them for this. Another problem was last-minute substitutions for volunteers who could not serve; the number of calls to get substitutes was overwhelming.

As chairman of the mental health committee, I recommended early in 1959 that we employ a part-time professional to coordinate the program and supervise and schedule the volunteers. Later that year we hired our first part-time staff member, a social worker.

Philosophy, purpose, policy

Even though Council House has grown and developed substantially during the thirteen years since it was created, its essential purpose remains the same: to provide educative and membership experiences to people who have had serious mental illness, primarily in the hope that the Council House affiliation will serve as a bridge between, on the one hand, the dependency and inadequacy that typically characterize life in the mental hospital, and, on the other hand, a capability to live an autonomous and productive life in the community. Over the years certain preferences, exclusions, and persuasions have developed.

Council House identifies as its target members "any ex-patients with some capability to interact in the program" and states its preference for "persons with schizophrenic reaction who have a little conflict-free ego to work with." Inevitably the concept of the agency varies somewhat from one staff member and referring agency to another. Some see the socialization functions as the most important aspect of the program. Others stress the significance of prevocational work experience and job placement. Some would prefer to see the agency as providing a transitional service, and therefore as a temporary, although perhaps lengthy, episode in the ex-patient's life history, while others, in sharp contrast with some other centers, appear to be comfortable in viewing the service as a terminal and potentially lifelong placement for many of the members. Some see its major impact as preventive of chronic and/or severe disability resulting from mental illness.

Dr. Jack Wolford, psychiatric consultant to Council House, characterizes it as the "only program in Pittsburgh totally devoted to tertiary prevention." He emphasizes the program's attempt to work with the conflict-free portion of the ego—an expression heard many times during our visit to Council House. It may be well here to spell out the Council House concept of this metaphorical approach to the personality of the schizophrenic. The ego may be conceived of as having *synthetic* functions and *executive* functions. The synthetic, or conflict-born, portion of the ego evolves from a negotiation or struggle or conflict between the id and the superego culminating in a compromise about how they will get along with each other. In the schizophrenic the conflict is typically destructive, and the compromise typically unsuccessful and unsatisfactory. In contrast, the executive, or conflict-free, portion develops from intrinsic biological predispositions and is concerned with such ordinary life activities as talking, walking, and eating. The synthetic portion is therefore conceptualized as involved in the schizophrenic disorder, while the executive portion is viewed as essentially conflict-free, or as the healthy part of the patient. To put it another way, historically the schizophrenic person, because he may have been incompetent in some areas of living, was viewed as incompetent in all areas. Dr. Wolford, Mrs. Lois R. Evey, who is the director of Council House, and many of their associates accept the premise that the executive functions can be differentiated from the illness, are essentially free of it, and therefore can be "worked with" to impart to the member some of the behavior and performance skills that he needs and must have in order to survive in and be accepted by the general society. To go one further step, the conflicted portions of the ego may not even be amenable to treatment given the present resources and state-of-the-art, and the conflict may very well persist; but this need not eventuate, as in recent history it often has, in the removal of the schizophrenic from the general society into a total institution.

Moving forward from this approach to service, we discussed at length with the Council House staff whether it is appropriate to consider their program as "therapy" within the consensual but constantly changing boundaries of that term. Said Mrs. Evey:

> We consider that any interaction resulting in growth or insight is therapeutic, and hence therapy. Our staff members interact with our members in this fashion, even though we do not provide any form of formal psychotherapy. We consider our focus on the conflict-free portion of the ego to be therapeutic, just so long as our clients make advances and do not regress.

Dr. Wolford elaborated on this theme.

> I think of everything we do as therapeutic. Any experience that helps the patient move forward, be it microscopically, is a therapeutic experience. If a member drops in at our offices and the secretary doesn't know how to deal with him appropriately, that is antitherapeutic, and we must teach the secretary how to be therapeutic.

Mrs. Evey points out that every component of the Council House program has been deliberately developed out of perceived need.

> We ourselves saw the need for the social program, and that is what led to the creation of Council House. But as we helped people to stay out of hospitals, eventually their families were more and more saying to them, "Why aren't you working? We're tired of taking care of you." So the members came to us asking whether we couldn't help

them get jobs. Consequently we began the prevocational training plus a limited placement service. Then with experience we began to realize that many of the rehospitalizations took place over the weekends. In those days there were no community clinics and the doctors were not always available after five o'clock on Friday. So we put in an emergency telephone service, operating from five in the evening until nine in the morning on weekdays and all the time on weekends and holidays.

The concept of the program as tertiary prevention is of course taken from the American Public Health Association's concept of primary, secondary, and tertiary prevention. These concepts have been subject to considerable reinterpretation over the years, and consequently we asked Dr. Wolford to define tertiary prevention as the term applies at Council House. He said:

Tertiary prevention means cutting down the residual defects or deficits, and the formation of positive aspects in people who are sick and/or disabled and likely to remain so. Applied to a particular individual, a suitable synonym is *rehabilitation*. The social interchanges that we provide to patients, regardless with whom, are a part of tertiary prevention—interactions that help them to cling to reality. The conflict-free ego is pretty small in many of our members, so we have to work all the harder. In the long-term schizophrenics who represent most of our clients, there are damages that are irreversible in terms of what we know today. Some of them are irreparably crippled. But many of them do have ego strength that has never been mobilized and put to use. This is what we try to mobilize. And this is why we deal as little as possible with the conflicted aspects of personality, about which we don't think we could do very much anyway.

Council House, perhaps more than some of the other centers, concerns itself with the *quality* of the lives of people who have been discharged to the community from mental hospitals. Dr. Wolford does not agree with those who think that any person with mental illness is, under any circumstances whatever, automatically better off in the community than he would be in hospital. "There are worse things than being hospitalized for life," he said, "and one of them is living in the community with no involvement in community life." He and his colleagues did a door-to-door canvass of formerly hospitalized mental patients and found "much to our horror and dismay" that the majority of them were sitting at home, hallucinating, not taking their medication, not having their medication given to them by their families. "We believe that many people, under these circumstances, would be better off back in the hospital. Furthermore, many of them said they would prefer to be back in the hospital."

Dr. Downey, superintendent of the state hospital that is the major source of referrals to Council House, agrees with Dr. Wolford. He has endorsed and supported Council House from the outset because its timely intervention may help the discharged patient to initiate community involvement at a crucial point.

> One of my patients told me some years ago that the lonesomest day of his life was the first day he was out of the hospital after discharge. The more I thought about this, the more I marveled that it had not already occurred to me. Council House is serving the mentally ill almost as Travelers Aid serves the ordinary citizen. I wonder why the mental health field has not generally realized that a kind of Travelers Aid is needed for the poor fellow who is being urged out of the hospital.

We interviewed a man who had been a Council House member for some years and had since become successfully employed and well established in a suburb of Pittsburgh.

> Over the years I tried for help at a lot of other agencies, but they were almost always evasive and never provided any direct help. What stands out in my mind about Council House is the immediate response always provided. One time when I ran off from my wife, I came to Council House, and they said, You need some sleep; you look like a wreck. So they got me a room at the YMCA, they called my wife and told her not to worry. They got me to a psychiatrist. Even now, several years after I stopped participating in their program, I know that if I got in a jam I could telephone them and they'd give me immediate help.

Mrs. Evey expressed the belief that Council House would never reach the point of cutting off service to anyone. "We feel the need to see our members move ahead and improve, and we do push them somewhat. But we always leave the door open so that they won't lose too much face if they have to come back after two or three years. Very few of them ever seem to have been ashamed of their affiliation with us. We see them on the street and they stop to chat. Many of them drop by from time to time to say hello. When they do have to come back, they don't seem to be uncomfortable about it."

Council House studies indicate that the rehospitalization rate for its members is considerably lower than for the general population of persons discharged from state hospitals (discussed below). This is viewed as justification for the effort and money that go into the program. But even if this were not the case, it seems probable that Council House would try to continue its services for whatever comfort and satisfaction they provide its members. "We think we are helping," said Mrs. Evey, "but in any case I don't think we could possibly be hurting. If our members can live in the community, take comfort from knowing that we are here to help them if they have an emergency, are glad for them to drop by whenever they feel like it, then we have to feel that we are not hurting. They'll say to us, 'I almost called you the other day, but I knew you were there and I thought I'd try to work it out for myself.' "

There are particular categories of persons coming from mental hospitals that Council House for the most part avoids or screens very carefully. These include:

• Alcoholics. If the primary diagnosis is alcoholism, Council House prefers that they deal with other agencies in Pittsburgh. This is in part because of past experiences in which alcoholics have seemed to behave in ways that "further impose on the weak egos of our schizophrenic members."

• Epileptics. Council House asks that seizures have been under medical control for at least six months. Epileptics are felt to run a greater risk than others of injury and thus to put the program under greater liability. Also, the alarm that a seizure may generate in the personnel of the agencies that provide space to Council House might lead to the loss of a meeting facility. Finally, Council House has found that referring agencies have often refused or neglected to provide adequate information about epileptics; in one dramatic case an epileptic had a seizure while in the swimming pool during a Council House swimming party, and, without quick action of staff, could easily have drowned.

• Drug addicts. Addicts are screened out for essentially the same reasons as are alcoholics.

• Severely retarded. Council House feels that other agencies in Pittsburgh are better equipped to provide care for the retarded.

• Sociopaths. "They can be so destructive that everyone else suffers; furthermore, a disproportionate amount of staff time is required to set limits for them."

Management and administration

Council House currently has a seventeen-member policy-making lay board of trustees which is in the process of expanding to a thirty-member board. It is their wish to have membership include representatives from as many areas of the "community" as possible to help bring a variety of interests, skills, and values. Currently, elementary and higher education, law, small business, industry, and journalism are represented. One medical doctor, the wife of an industrial psychiatrist, is a member. Two members are doctors' wives; they have been involved in the advancement of community mental health for many years through the Pennsylvania mental health association and other community groups. Three are also members of the National Council of Jewish Women. They remain not only for their skills as community leaders, but also to reassure the National Council of Jewish Women of the continuity of their original, tremendous investment. The clergy is represented by a Catholic priest and a minister from the black community. The newest additions to the board are three Council House volunteers who have been particularly active.

The board, which is a "working" as well as an administrative group, meets monthly. The group typically concerns itself with policy making, fund raising, publicity, promoting community education and involvement, and lobbying for better mental health policies. Fiscal problems tend to get greatest priority, since stable funding has been elusive.

There is also a thirteen-member professional advisory committee which has existed from the time Council House was established. It includes, ideally, at least two representatives from each professional discipline related to community mental health and meets twice a year. Its members are consulted when drastic or dramatic changes in program, philosophy, or policies are anticipated. For example, their advice was sought on the current plans to "decentralize" Council House programs into the ten catchment areas into which the county has been divided under the new Allegheny County Mental Health and Mental Retardation Program.

Physical facilities

In contrast to the other five centers, Council House does not have, and professes not to want, its own physical facilities for conducting its program. Instead it limits its premises to a suite of offices for the staff, with space for the intake process and some counseling. Most of the direct program activities—social and recreational programs, prevocational training, and such physical fitness programs as swimming and volleyball—are all conducted in community centers, schools, churches, social and civic agencies, YM/YWHA's, YMCA's, etc. Of approximately forty different loci at the time of our visit, only three made a charge for the meeting space. In recent years, as Council House has moved toward providing the tertiary prevention or rehabilitation component for some of the newly emerging community mental health centers, there has been a move toward decentralizing still further, i.e., away from the downtown area and into some of the suburban parts of Allegheny County.

The offices of Council House are located in downtown Pittsburgh on the sixth floor of a building well past its prime; the access is via a small and dilapidated elevator. The offices have been nicely remodeled, with paneling in all the rooms and bright, cheerful furnishings. Despite the disclaimer Council House makes about having its own service area, a portion of the offices has been designated as a lounge area for patients. This is primarily for use of persons waiting for an "intake" interview, counseling, or evaluation for some other supportive service such as referral to another community facility, supportive casework, or possibly a total plan for a day's activity seen as daycare support. There are comfortable chairs, magazines, and some games, and the coffee urn is always in operation. A number of Council House members drop by every day to rest, to chat, or to read, and the volume of such visits has grown in recent years. During our visit there were patients in the lounge at all times of the day. There were about fifteen in the late afternoon; these were persons involved in the "work" program who stopped in between work and the social programs which are held in different community settings.

The philosophy opposing the acquisition of a building for program activities has many interesting implications, particularly that it stresses the community *qua* community as the locus for rehabilitation efforts, rather than the facilities of a specific organization. Too, it is seen by staff as the easiest way to educate large areas of the community in an effort to eliminate the stigma attached to mental illness. Council House has maintained, ever since the time that it began to expand beyond a once-weekly ex-patient social club, that it is preferable for its members to participate in activities on the same premises that nonmental patients do, where there are programs that might eventually involve particular Council House members who no longer need the sheltered activities that Council House provides to them. Because of budget problems and growth problems, it may also be that the option toward community settings was to some extent a matter of expedience, but in any case it is an interesting concept. All at Council House believe that a program of this proportion would be virtually impossible to fund without the donation of extensive community resources. It will be interesting to see in the years ahead whether it is modified, as Council House becomes more established and confident financially in its role as rehabilitation arm of the newly developing community mental health centers.

The staff

Council House is staffed by an executive director, two full-time case-workers, a part-time caseworker, a group worker, a director of program and volunteers, a rehabilitation counselor, a psychiatric nurse, and two mental health aides, plus supporting clerical and secretarial personnel.

The director, Mrs. Evey, who has a master's degree in nursing edu-cation as a clinical specialist in psychiatric nursing, came to Council House in 1962 as a psychiatric nurse and became the director in 1965. She appears to be a thoughtful, capable person who as an administrator has her finger on everything that goes on.

The staff told us that there is only an informal hierarchy, "with no particular pecking order." The senior and supervising caseworker came to Council House after working in a family and children's service else-where in Pittsburgh, but he knew the Council House program from a field placement there during his graduate work.

The other full-time caseworker is assigned to Council House by West-ern Psychiatric Institute and Clinic, a federally assisted community men-tal health center, in connection with the contract that Council House has entered into with WPIC to provide rehabilitation services. A native of the Netherlands, she came to WPIC directly from her graduate train-ing and was immediately assigned to Council House. She handles much of the intake for prospective Council House members, with first priority going to people who live in the catchment area served by the mental health center. In addition to running a relatively new special group established for younger members of Council House, those between sev-enteen and thirty, she spends most of her time in casework, sometimes on a scheduled basis but more often informally.

The rehabilitation counselor had joined the staff a few months prior to our visit. He is principally responsible for a large variety of activities related to the work program. More recently he has been assigned the role of liaison Council House staff with the Homestead Hospital Com-munity Mental Health Center. (Each staff member has at least five per-cent of his time allotted to a liaison role with one of the ten evolving catchment areas in the county.)

There is also a director of program and volunteers, who has been with the agency for several years. Her principal responsibilities are to recruit volunteers from the community, to oversee the development of new pro-grams, to get free tickets for the members, and to "deal with the com-munity in a public relations capacity."

In 1968, Council House attempted to collaborate with St. Francis Hospital in developing a program to train mental health aides who had completed a ten-week course of preliminary mental health education at the hospital. When financial problems made it impossible to hire any of the aides into the Council House program, a grant was made available by the Falk Medical Fund whereby two trainees from poverty areas of Pittsburgh who had completed the ten-week St. Francis program came to Council House to learn methods of providing social rehabilitation for the mentally ill.

We interviewed one of these aides, an attractive, articulate young Negro girl. "In our ten weeks at St. Francis we were given just an edge of what mental illness was, including some material about symptoms and the different ways we should act if we were confronted by someone who was mentally ill," she told us. "We did role-playing interviews, wrote reports, and so on."

She spends much of her time in the work program, helping members with their work assignments, intervening in any crisis that arises, encouraging those who do not feel up to working, and often going along with them to their job assignments and working alongside them. In terms of the population of Pittsburgh, Council House is underrepresented in Negro members, and this mental health aide has tried to establish closer relationships with the black community. Said one of the consultants:

> This young woman certainly seems to be a loving and kind person. She recognizes that the Council House members need much reassurance, and that complimenting them on their performance over a long period of time can sometimes result in their doing things spontaneously. In her assignment of heading up the charm class, it thrills her to see the improvement in the women when they have their hair done and learn to use cosmetics.

Another important role of the mental health aide at Council House is to work under the supervision of a specified professional staff member in reaching out to "dropouts" and "uninvolved referrals." Each is assigned at least two catchment areas. Home visits are made, problems are identified, limited health teaching is done. Often the aides escort members to the clinic, Council House programs, shopping, and so on.

This initial training program, for the two aides, was seen to be so effective by all involved at Council House that plans are being presented in the 1970-71 budget to make formal training of indigenous workers a part of the program. Currently, five trainees are involved through a cooperative effort with Community Action Pittsburgh. Two are from a community action program—New Careers—made possible through the Department of Labor. They will stay for two years and will be earning an associate degree—Social Work Technician—from Allegheny Community College. The other three are from another community action program, Operation Mainstream. They will train at Council House, on a comprehensive level, for one year and will become mental health aides, either to be hired by Council House or other community mental health facilities. Council House has presented a plan to the Allegheny County Mental Health and Mental Retardation Program to provide a formal educational program for mental health aides to help staff evolving community mental health centers.

T HE COUNCIL HOUSE STAFF seem well trained, enthusiastic, energetic, and committed. This seems to be particularly true of the executive director, who gives the impression that she would do anything in her power to help a member in need. The staff readily accept the appropriateness of working with an admittedly difficult group, as well as the importance of the services they provide. While there is some specialization of labor, there is also a great deal of "role blurring," with most staff members performing a variety of functions. One senses an attitude of flexibility and idealism, plus a real concern about doing more within and outside of Council House in the hope of making a genuine difference in the lives of the members.

Volunteers

Having started as a volunteer effort, Council House continues to make extensive use of volunteers. There are approximately sixty-five who are active, with about half this number contributing the bulk of volunteer time, which comes to about one hundred hours per week. Most of the volunteers are women; efforts to recruit men have not been very successful. Volunteers are for the most part well educated and from higher social and economic strata. They are recruited both individually and through church and club affiliations. Most who sign on either drop out rather soon or else continue to be active for a considerable period of time, often for several years.

The director of volunteers said that she has been highly selective in screening applicants. Each is interviewed for about an hour in the interest of determining that she seems reasonably healthy and not "overly outgoing." Volunteers are discouraged from associating with members other than in the course of their assigned participation at Council House.

Besides four weeks of involvement in program activities prior to their acceptance of and by Council House, each new volunteer is required to attend a four-week orientation program conducted twice each year by Dr. Wolford.

Council House conceptualizes four particular types of volunteer needs and recruits and assigns them accordingly.

There are *all-purpose* volunteers, those who have limited time available but who can come to special programs when extra help is needed, provide transportation, bake cakes for parties, go shopping with members who need to learn how to buy, visit members who have been rehospitalized, who will donate clothing and solicit gifts from friends, and be on call for emergencies. All-purpose volunteers are not expected to be able to answer every call, but are often available on short notice and will respond if other obligations do not interfere.

Specialized-service volunteers are persons able to accept a specific and regular assignment. A number of these regularly attend the Monday night "large group" socials either each week or alternate weeks. They are expected *a*) to come on time, *b*) to give adequate notice when they cannot come, *c*) to participate in periodic staff-volunteer meetings to evaluate the programs in which they are active, and *d*) to write brief reports when requested to do so by the program leader.

Program leaders are volunteers with special skills plus leadership abilities who are willing to assume direct responsibility for running programs in conjunction with staff members. Program leaders are assigned to a dance class, a sewing and alterations class, a charm and grooming clinic, a nutrition program, a "fix-it" program, a job clinic, and a discussion group.

Council House also uses volunteers to help in *administrative aspects* of the program, including office work, public relations, and fund raising.

There have been no difficulties or problems with volunteers beyond those typically experienced by mental health programs. These include the tendency of an occasional volunteer to become overinvolved with a particular member, and a flagging of interest when the members turn out to be less stimulating than the volunteer had anticipated, or when a crisis is taken to the volunteer, instead of staff, and she tries to handle the situation rather than refer it to the staff.

The clientele

Council House works mostly with chronic patients who have had repeated hospitalizations. Each successive hospitalization is considered to have contributed to the member's inadequacy and his tendency toward chronicity. It follows that the rehabilitation potential for many of these patients would ordinarily be viewed as quite low. Many who have achieved something before they became ill may be afraid to try again for fear of failure. On the other hand, those who have not achieved anything before their illness have little previous useful experience on which to base their efforts and thus are also afraid to try.

Mrs. Evey believes that the better developed the member was before he became ill the better he will do, unless he is unable or unwilling to reach towards this higher goal. Several reasons for this kind of unwillingness have been noted. The youthful schizophrenic seems to be the worst prospect precisely because he has so little in his past experience to draw on. Those who were on their way up, and therefore motivated, when they became ill, appear to have the best prognosis. People who are on welfare or disability pensions often fear that by performing well they will lose their financial security and thus are very difficult to motivate.

Eligibility. Any person with a history of mental illness and evidently in need of socialization and/or vocational help is eligible for referral to the Council House program. The majority of those who are referred or who apply as a self-referral are accepted. Those who are rejected include persons who appear to be too regressed to have any potential to benefit from the program, those who seem potentially assaultive, those with major physical health problems or organic brain disease, those with histories of homosexual acting out, or those with a primary diagnosis of alcoholism or narcotic addiction; but *in toto* these represent relatively few of the applicants to Council House. Because such persons are screened out, expulsions for misbehavior are infrequent; when they do occur, it is on the decision of staff rather than fellow members, even though these decisions are made upon observation of interruption of program or trauma to an individual or group. A steering committee helps in establishing rules of dress and basic rules for appropriate behavior.

Diagnosis. Council House does not always have much formal information about the diagnoses of the members. While no particular emphasis is placed on diagnosis as such, Council House would like to have more information than it does. State and federal statistical reports sometimes require such information. The shortage is usually due to the reluctance of referring agencies to furnish the information. Some have told Council House that they want applicants accepted "as persons," but in some cases it may be because medical agencies are reluctant to furnish such information to an agency that they may view as nonmedical (despite the intricate involvement of Dr. Wolford as psychiatric consultant). Even so, Council House is persuaded that the vast majority of its members—more than ninety percent—are persons who have been diagnosed as schizophrenic. This seems logical for the simple reason that schizophrenics represent the substantial majority of mentally ill persons who need the kind of services they provide.

Referral sources. Prospective members often hear about Council House before they are discharged, usually by word of mouth from members, doctors, other hospital staff members, or visiting Council House staff and volunteers. Much of this occurs during a special program scheduled once a month, called "inhospital night." Patients thought to be near discharge are entertained in a community setting by members, staff, and volunteers of Council House. Three local state hospitals, two private psychiatric hospitals, and one new "restoration" facility send patients to this program, which has the goal of familiarizing patients with a community agency that can help to bridge the gap from hospital to community living. Council House has found that members are much easier to keep involved if they have been given an opportunity to learn of its services and programs *before* they leave the hospital.

The largest statistical category of referrals—27 percent—is the self-referred, but these include many persons who have been in the agencies and institutions that customarily refer to Council House, and who come without a formal referral. The next largest category—2i percent—is those referred by state hospitals. General hospitals send five percent. The remaining 47 percent are referred from a large number of other sources: two community mental health centers, the state vocational rehabilitation agency, psychiatrists in private practice, the county health department, a residential service called Transitional Services, Inc., ministers, the state employment service, the welfare department, and by relatives, friends, and present members.

Age and sex distribution. Women outnumber men in a ratio of three to two. Very few of the members—five percent—are under 21, and 11 percent are over 60. The remaining 84 percent, those between 21 and 60, are fairly evenly distributed by age.

Because the younger members had complained that there were too many older members in most of the groups, a special youth group was established, to be run by the members, in the hope that left to themselves the young people would show some initiative. This did not happen, and consequently an executive committee of the more integrated younger members was successfully set up. Since this was planned to be a "group" instead of a "program," acceptance of referrals has been limited to approximately twenty. This allows supervising staff an opportunity to deal more effectively with group dynamics and provide for more adequate learning situations. Currently, a larger number of referrals is being received and plans are being discussed to start an additional program in the fall. One group will serve members aged 17 to 25; the other, those who are 25 to 30. In this way, both can be group experiences and attendance can be maintained at a lower level deemed more effective and therapeutic. Council House feels the main problem with these young people is that they have become mentally ill before they have attained many skills, and while they range in age up to thirty are for the most part adolescent in attitude.

Residential status. Most Council House members live other than with parents, wives, husbands, and children. Some of the arrangements to live apart from families were made necessary "to allow the member an opportunity for growth and independence." However, in many cases the family pattern of living had been interrupted or destroyed by the effects of the illness. Often the member had been rejected by his family. Too, approximately 225 members are currently hospitalized since Council House serves not only persons living in the community but also those who are in varying stages of transition to community living, as well as those who have had to be rehospitalized. A large majority of those living alone rent only a room in a private home or a rooming house, or share an apartment. Foster home arrangements are made for many of the members who are veterans, by the Veterans Administration Hospital staff. Recently, increasing numbers of members are being referred to and through Transitional Services, Inc., which was established in 1966 to provide halfway house and transitional apartment living arrangements for both men and women.*

Employment status. Data on employment status of members were available only for newly admitted members, most of whom are not working at all during their first months of membership. About seven percent are employed either full time or part time in competitive employment and another 14 percent are employed full time or part time in various sheltered settings. The remaining 79 percent are not working, although many of these are women who are not in the labor market.

Intake

Becoming a member at Council House is an informal, uncomplicated process. If the referral is by telephone from an agency or hospital, Council

---

*The program of Transitional Services, Inc., is described in R. M. Glasscote, J. E. Gudeman, and J. R. Elpers: *Halfway Houses for the Mentally Ill: A Study of Programs and Problems.* The Joint Information Service, Washington, D. C., 1971.

House asks that a referral form be completed and sent in. Once the form is received, or if the applicant has himself applied, some member of the Council House staff telephones him to schedule an appointment. While certain staff members handle more referrals than others, there are several members of the staff who handle some, depending both on available time and on particular indicated needs; that is, if a work program seemed particularly indicated, the intake would probably be done by the vocational counselor.

There is no brochure describing the program, and the only prepared material given to the applicant is a copy of the current issue of the Council House newsletter, which includes a schedule of the month's events. A detailed kit of descriptive materials is available for professional staff of referring agencies, students, and interested community persons.

At the intake interview, which is relatively brief and unthreatening, the customary "social service content" is avoided. Council House programs are described to the applicant in an attempt to elicit some expression of his interest and plans.

Thereafter, at the four-hour weekly staff meeting, the intake worker exchanges his impressions with the rest of the staff and the psychiatric consultant; the applicant's history and background are presented, and some agreement is reached about how or whether Council House might serve him. We have described the usual reasons for rejecting an applicant.

If he is accepted, the intake worker gets in touch with him and in most cases invites him to start attending programs right away. New members are usually scheduled for the large Monday evening social meeting. Some who seem to be threatened by so large a group are scheduled instead for a Wednesday evening meeting that stresses recreation and athletic events and is usually attended by about thirty. If there has been some expression of interest in a particular activity, the new member might be scheduled for that group as well, or he might "graduate" to it after a period of time in the Monday or Wednesday evening programs.

Once particular programs are recommended, the staff and volunteers are alerted that the new member is coming. He is observed closely at Monday evening meetings, and the plan for him may be changed if this seems to be indicated; such changes might be to place him in the work program and/or assign him to a caseworker for individual counseling. However, new members are not ordinarily "assigned" in the casework sense to particular members of the staff; this is done on the basis of a developed member-staff relationship, or on the assigned basis of the person thought best able to bring about effective change.

This easy and informal process of intake, evaluation, assignment, and follow-up seems attractive in that it minimizes threat to the applicant, counteracts the traditional social agency or clinic climate, establishes a "social club feeling," and is administratively easy to execute. A possible problem inherent in it may be its reliance on the ex-patient's own motivation, in some cases thereby insufficiently stimulating him to participate. This is kept in constant attention by staff, however, and "reaching out" is done to those thought to need it.

Council House appears to feel that some lapse of time may in fact foster greater involvement later on. In other words, the staff tend to believe that after the ex-patient has experienced some discouragement and disappointment in his postdischarge life he may be better motivated for a program of the Council House sort.

Dropouts. Council House pursues any member who drops out of the program. Said Mrs. Evey, "We have always made it our responsibility to check on members until we are sure that their leaving the program is based on strengths and gains and not on illness." The initial contact is made by telephone, if possible. A home visit is made if indicated and accepted by the member involved. A questionnaire is used to gain information for future reference. It asks *a*) the kinds of help the member got in the process of making contact with Council House and whether he felt the referring agency was helpful, *b*) whether the Council House program was accurately described to him, *c*) what image he had of the agency, *d*) the frequency and kinds of participation, *e*) whether there were family problems that interfered with participation, *f*) whether some special arrangements could be made that would enable him to resume participation, and *g*) which of a large number of indicated reasons account for his dropping out.

In an analysis of dropouts, Council House has identified three principal categories. The first are those who are uninvolved because of *intrapersonal factors,* predominantly anomie, apathy, and withdrawal, with inability to mobilize for participation in employment, health maintenance, and socialization. The individuals in this category are often unable to travel alone. Their lack of motivation to become involved in their surroundings is primarily identified as resulting from impairment from internal sources. Related to this are the dropouts who are uninvolved because of intrapsychic factors, particularly denial of illness, including unwillingness to be viewed as a mental patient.

The second category are those who drop out because of *social factors,* best represented by the person "who returns to a symbiotic relationship and is so overprotected that he is prevented from engaging in activities independent of the family."

The third category consists of those who are *involved in other outside activities*. Such people have no evident overt symptoms of illness and have made some independent effort to interact successfully with their environment. This category includes the seemingly functioning housewife and the person who has returned to work and/or resumed activity with a social organization.

"No-shows." As with most other social agencies, Council House has a large percentage of referrals who do not come at all or who come only for the initial interview and drop out without having been accepted as members. A survey of referrals made several years ago revealed that 37 percent either did not contact Council House or came once only. This group was analyzed in terms of the psychiatric and rehabilitation needs that had led to the referral. Said a paper describing Council House*:

> It became obvious that, in the absence of alternate resources to meet these needs, it was likely that a group of persons was being identified, who, having bypassed Council House, were not receiving any social rehabilitation services at all, even though some maintained psychiatric clinic contacts. . . . Some patients were receiving no services at all.

A questionnaire is used with the "no-shows." It is approximately the same as the one mentioned above for dropouts.

The program, in general

Of the three principal components that we sought in our search for psychosocial agencies—that is, socialization, vocational, and residential services—Council House provides large amounts of the social and vocational. By design, it provides little of the residential, since its aim is to help the reintegration of the member into the community. Although Council House provides no medication, it has set up arrangements for members to obtain medication at reduced rates. In addition to the social and vocational services Council House operates a 24-hour telephone crisis service for its members.

Throughout the program the emphasis is on interactions among members and between members and staff with almost no pressuring to fit

---

*J. A. Wolford and P. Roberts: "Council House: The Natural History of a Social Rehabilitation Center," *British Journal of Social Psychiatry* 1:3:226-236, Summer 1967.

into a formal structure or to capitalize on the common bond of their illness. The staff members are seen as stabilizers, ego ideals, and catalysts.

There are no written rules, but consensual rules do exist. Infractions are dealt with by group pressure or, if that does not prove sufficient, by the intervention of some particular staff member. "Those who exhibit grossly inappropriate behavior are temporarily suspended from that particular program 'for the good of the greatest number' and for the individual member's own good, since he must learn that his behavior was not socially acceptable," Mrs. Evey told us.

There is a steering committee which does not so much constitute a patient government as it does a self-governing group within Council House. This steering committee proved difficult to motivate "since it attacks the very basic dependency that influences the ability of the mentally ill to be rehabilitated." The group faltered on its first two attempts and shortly before our visit had been started a third time under the direction of the group worker. Representatives had been elected from the total membership, but the leaders had not sufficiently stabilized to elect officers. The principal activities include a committee to provide hosts for the Monday evening social program and the Wednesday evening programs, and to help stabilize the monthly "inhospital night" hosts and hostesses committee, a house committee to help keep the offices and lounge area neat, and a clean-up committee that helps to clear up following various of the community activities.

Time limit. Council House feels that it constantly encourages members to be independent and to spin off into the larger community, but is unwilling to set a time limit. For one thing, many members have not developed and show no immediate prospect of developing other community ties after such periods as six months or a year. "Since there is no other program for him to go into, if we stopped his participation we would be encouraging him to remain ill," we were told.

A second major reason is the inability, expressed by most of the Council House staff and by Dr. Wolford, to predict who is going to become independent and how long it will take. Said Mrs. Evey:

> We believe that if one gives members say, ninety days, many of them wouldn't bother. Since they think they can't make it in that time, they wouldn't try at all. On the other hand, we have seen people who have been members here for five years and longer suddenly make dramatic progress.

Memberships are not, however, held open forever. In order to be considered active, one must have had some contact, however minimal, with Council House during the year prior to an annual review that takes place. Using this criterion, Council House numbers its active members at approximately 1200, of whom approximately 500 participate to some extent within a given month.

Social and recreation program

Council House lists among its social activities some events, for example a construction workshop for men, that other programs might consider prevocational, but we shall use the same classification as Council House. Approximately eighty social and recreational events were scheduled for a month in early 1970. The majority of these took place once a week, a few once, twice, or three times a month.

The weekly events included:

• Charm class

• A "supper club" that meets at a downtown cafeteria and a second one that meets on a different night in one of the new county catchment areas

• The youth group already described in part, which meets in the conference room of the local mental health association

• The large Monday night program, often attended by more than one hundred persons, at the YWCA. A second one, much smaller in attendance, has been started in one of the new county catchment areas on a different evening.

• Swimming and volleyball at a suburban YM/YWHA

• Health club for men at the University of Pittsburgh field house

• "Fun night" at another YM/YWHA

• "Slimnastics" for women at a local nurses' home gymnasium

• An arts and crafts program held in a large church lounge in a suburban area

• Job clinic

• A bridge club in the conference room of the Pittsburgh National Bank

• Sewing class in a suburban community center

• A current events club at the downtown YMCA cafeteria-lounge

• A friendship committee that sends cards to sick members

The only biweekly program is a construction workshop held at one of the junior high schools.

Events that take place one, two, or three times a month include a planning meeting of the steering committee, at the YWCA; a "mates and dates night" for couples only, at the Lutheran University Center; an "inhospital night," at the YWCA; luncheon meetings of the steering committee, at the Council House offices; a "Kaffeeklatsch," at a civic club; bowling, at a suburban bowling alley; and picnics.

There are many other classes and events that take place seasonally or at stated intervals, including nutrition clinic, homemaking, first aid, home nursing, "fix-it" program, and mothers' helpers classes. Tickets are frequently available for, and members sometimes attend in a group, baseball games, the county fair, boat rides, variety shows, the light opera, professional football, skating parties, basketball games, the symphony, the opera, plays, wrestling matches, hockey games, movies, the circus, the auto show, the boat show, the ice follies, a folk festival, etc. There are overnight camping trips, industrial, historic, and sight-seeing tours, a hay ride and square dance at Halloween, covered dish suppers at Thanksgiving and Easter, and a Christmas party. Car washing and bake sales are scheduled from time to time to allow members to earn bus fare to get to Council House activities. The Christmas party is believed significant since it is held on Christmas afternoon when most staff, volunteers, board members, etc. would wish to be with their own families. It is remembered, however, that many Council House members have no families and would miss out on this significant holiday. Thus, it is made a big "family party."

To a large extent the more chronic and regressed members are intermixed with the more integrated members, although some care must be taken not to overload the group with members functioning at the lowest level. Said Mrs. Evey:

> The advantage of a mix is that the sick people can see the well people and can say, You made it and so I ought to be able to. For this reason we use some of our more capable members as volunteers during the inhospital night; most of them have become fairly autonomous, so they come back to plan the program, serve the food, and mingle with the people from the hospital.

While the recreation activities are manifold, there is also strong emphasis on learning basic living skills. The nutrition clinic, for example, teaches budget management, buying for and preparing balanced, appetizing meals, decorating, etc. The sewing and alterations class is led by three particularly skilled volunteers who teach the members to stretch their money for clothing by changing sizes, styles, etc., and then to purchase materials and patterns.

A highly experienced volunteer directs a Saturday program, with a staff member attending as consultant, on the assumption that this is likely to be one of the deadliest times of the week for people who have nothing to do. In season this group goes to athletic events, and at other times there are lectures by guests from a variety of fields.

Council House has mobilized support from many community agencies. As we have mentioned, almost all of the many meeting places are made available without charge. There are special periodic events, such as a quarterly bingo evening sponsored by a church group, which buys all the gifts. A bakery provides refreshments for weekly Wednesday evening programs. Over five hundred gifts are donated each year to be used as Christmas gifts to hospital members.

We have described some of the difficulties experienced with a relatively new group for younger members. A caseworker told us of a recent event at which the members went to a Chinese restaurant.

> They were forced to look at each other, to talk with each other. I was leery about it, but it went much better than I had expected.

Mrs. Evey discussed the particular problems of this group.

> With members who were perhaps thirty years old when they got sick, you can say, Remember your first date? But you say to a kid of eighteen, Remember your first date? and she didn't have one. You can't talk to them about the time they went to the prom, because they never went. You can't talk about the party they had for their birthday, because they never had a birthday party. In this youth group we're dealing with people who have to be taught to read a menu when they go to a restaurant. They're so uncomfortable with each other that we had to eliminate the initial planning meeting and substitute a social activity.

Vocational program

The work program at Council House is a Personal Adjustment Training Program carried out under contract with the Pennsylvania Bureau of Vocational Rehabilitation. Participants are chosen by the treating agency and formally referred for membership at Council House with a specific recommendation for the work program. Council House staff and the staff of the Bureau of Vocational Rehabilitation work jointly in evaluating the member for this program.

The period is stipulated at 13 weeks, but the substantial majority of clients need a renewal, and consequently about 90 percent engage in the program for 26 weeks. New members are given an orientation in the Council House office on the day they report for work, and are escorted to the job location. New members spend two days per week in their placements, while advanced members may spend up to five days as their work tolerance increases. Council House is the only agency in the area that starts clients on the two-day-per-week level to allow for a very basic beginning for approaching work.

In order to avoid conflict with labor unions, the work settings are primarily in 21 voluntary agencies such as the tuberculosis league and the heart and cancer societies. In the recent past some small private businesses, churches, and church-sponsored nursing homes have been added as placements. The Council House office is also used to teach office and household cleaning. The ultimate aim of this undertaking is motivation to return to work through opportunities for work training or retraining, but before this can be done, members who have experienced a long period of hospitalization may have to acquire or reacquire good work habits, as well as social skills and graces. They may need to relearn such simple skills as proper dress, getting to work on time, and the management of normal pressures that exist on every job.

The distinctive feature of Council House's Personal Adjustment Training is the fact that it takes place in normal places of employment. Ex-patients work together with regular employees, meeting the usual employment standards as closely as possible. There is no "sheltered workshop" atmosphere.

Each agency accepting Council House placements has a "supervisor," some member of the staff who will accompany clients to the job and stay with them if necessary, as it often is. Too, the participating agency provides a "boss" who gives work assignments, instructions, and corrections to provide an opportunity to learn the responsibility of relating to authority, taking directions, keeping time, etc.

Considering the training aspect, and to avoid the suggestion that a substandard "wage" is being offered, Council House has instead included an "incentive pay" feature which ranges from $8 to $14 a week.

There are weekly meetings of the work program staff to consider the clients' progress. Monthly reports must be submitted to the Bureau of Vocational Rehabilitation, using a form called "work habits and performance," which covers 26 criteria. These reports are also sent to the treating agency and hospital staff department heads.

About a quarter of those who participate in the program eventually go to full-time or part-time competitive employment, usually in menial jobs. An additional quarter move on to other specialized but longer-term vocational settings such as the Goodwill Industries and the Vocational Rehabilitation Center. About a quarter go to some formal training, including schooling, and the other 25 percent remain ill and many of them require rehospitalization.

At any one time approximately thirty Council House members are involved in the work program, and a number of these are persons who start on the program while still in hospital, in the hope that they can progress to the point of discharge and regular membership in Council House, as many of them do.

Residential program

Council House does not need to provide specialized living arrangements for its members because of the activities of Transitional Services, Inc., a comprehensive program that was started in 1966 by the local mental health association and has since become independent. Transitional Services operates halfway houses that intermix the mentally ill and the mentally retarded, and a series of apartments, to which people may be assigned either directly or after having lived at the halfway house.

Medication

Substantially all Council House members are taking psychotropic medication, which appears to be readily available both in terms of dispensing facilities and money to pay for it. Those who live in a catchment area where a community mental health center is operating may go there for prescriptions, which are then filled at local pharmacies. Others may go to the Allegheny County Mental Health and Mental Retardation Program office which provides the same service. If the person is on welfare, or is working but classed as medically indigent, he can receive the drugs without charge.

A crisis service

Since 1962 Council House has operated a 24-hour emergency crisis intervention service. As we have described, Council House soon learned that many of the rehospitalizations of its members took place on weekends, when little treatment service was available except a return to the state hospital. Consequently it established a telephone service, manned at night and on weekends by staff members on a rotating duty roster.

At least thirty "off hour" telephone calls are received each month. Many of these concern routine matters, but a few are genuine distress calls from members or their families, ranging from expressions of despair and loneliness to suicide threats. The psychiatric consultant backs up the staff member but now receives only about one call per week.

The telephone service serves the obvious need of an escape valve for a member in distress, which can if necessary bring immediate appropriate intervention, and in addition expresses very tangibly the accessibility and presence of Council House—"you're only a telephone call away"—which is an important ingredient in Council House's assessment of its helping role.

Mrs. Evey, who had been on telephone duty the night before our visit, described a call she had received. The caller was a Negro girl who had called on a number of previous occasions. She was married to a white man who mistreats her. Both families had cut them off because of objections to a mixed marriage. The girl had strong homicidal thoughts toward her husband. On this occasion, because of her considerable knowledge of the member, Mrs. Evey was able to conclude that the telephone call itself was sufficient, and consequently spent about thirty minutes talking with the girl and reassuring her; on some previous occasions Mrs. Evey has recommended that the girl go to the community mental health center for help.

Families

Many of the members of Council House do not have families "and this is one of the reasons they use Council House." For those that do, relatively little emphasis is placed on working with the family, in part because the limited amount of staff time is devoted to activities that have a higher priority, in part because the few efforts to date with families have not been very successful. Said a research report prepared by Council House:

> While the family may provide the basic requirements of food, clothing, and shelter, our data do not necessarily lead to the conclusion that the family as such is a therapeutic agent leading to improved integration of the patient.

In order to encourage greater independence of the members, families do not participate in Council House activities unless invited. Home visits are made, on request of the member or his family or a treating agency that is unable to make the visit itself, or because of some particular crisis; the member's permission is sought if it was not he himself who initiated the request.

Agency and community relationships

Several major aspects of the Council House program attest that it has developed superb relationships with numerous agencies both within and outside of the mental health field. Originally, as we have pointed out, there were problems: the professional community, other than Mayview State Hospital, tried to dissuade the Council of Jewish Women from starting the program, and in the early days it was extremely difficult to line up places to meet.

The professional community's acceptance is now evidenced by the plan for Council House to provide rehabilitation services for all of the ten community mental health centers planned for Allegheny County. The good quality of the relationship with state hospitals is seen in three of them sending predischarge patients to Council House activities in the hope that they will become involved, and in Council House members being welcomed at the hospitals in the hope that patients who see ex-patients who are functioning in the community will have raised morale. The attitude of the voluntary agency network is seen in the placements that more than a dozen of them provide for Council House members who are in the Personal Adjustment Training program. The attitude of civic groups and social organizations, the churches, and the schools is shown by the large number who make meeting and activity space available, almost all of them without charge.

This good state of affairs is the result of persistent effort, principally individual contacts by the staff of Council House, the board of trustees, and the volunteers.

Training

Council House is used by the graduate school of social work of the University of Pittsburgh as a field-work training unit. Also, the undergraduate school of social work of Pennsylvania State University places students at Council House for ten weeks of planned learning experiences. Students from the University of Pittsburgh graduate school of nursing come to Council House for experience in psychiatric nursing, as do undergraduate nursing students from the University of Pittsburgh, Duquesne University, and Carlow College. In 1967 the Washington (Pennsylvania) Hospital asked for a placement for students in their Generic School of Nursing; since then, the schools of nursing of Pittsburgh Hospital and Mercy Hospital have had similar arrangements for their students. Students in clinical psychology and psychiatric residency are given experience, as well as priests and other interested professionals who participate as observers, learners, and trainees from time to time. Expansion of these professional education services now includes vocational rehabilitation counselor trainees. Furthermore, if a currently planned agricultural nursery becomes a reality, Council House plans to submit a proposal to involve students from the Pennsylvania State University school of forestry and agriculture, as short-term participant-observers. It also hopes to involve students from the Mt. Aloysius College school of occupational therapy in the same project.

Each summer, under a Health and Welfare Association program called Careers in Social Work, three students are placed at Council House for three months as participant-observers. Also, the Job Corps has been placing approximately five students each summer for work as recreational aides and/or general office workers.

Finances

After the expiration of the National Institute of Mental Health grant, Council House experienced a severe financial crisis and was saved through interim support from local industrial, educational, and medical foundations. Then came a three-year period of support through the State Office of Mental Health grant-in-aid program, followed by the present arrangement with the Allegheny County Mental Health and Mental Retardation Program. Council House has been designated as the mental health agency to provide social rehabilitation for the mentally ill for the ten emerging catchment areas. The principal source of funds for Council House at present and in the foreseeable future will be the Allegheny County Mental Health and Mental Retardation Program and a purchase-of-service arrangement with the Bureau of Vocational Rehabilitation for the Personal Adjustment Training program.

The budget during the 1969-70 fiscal year was approximately $150,000. About $115,000—a great deal less than had been anticipated—came from the state funds channeled through the county mental health program. About $30,000 was projected in payments from the Bureau of Vocational Rehabilitation. The small balance, about $1500, came from gifts.

There were no charges for service until Council House became part of the community mental health center plan. The members themselves have never been charged fees. To do so was counter to the purposes and philosophy of the Council of Jewish Women in starting the project, and this attitude persists. However, under the new comprehensive mental health and mental retardation program, fees for service are required. Due to the complexity of Council House programs and services, a fee for service has been extremely difficult to determine. Thus, for the present, a $12 maximum fee per month was adopted which is to be a part of the member's total liability to the mental health program whether he be channeled into the continuum of services at Council House, a community mental health center, or another of the participating agencies. The total liability, of course, is based on ability to pay. Since approximately 85 percent of Council House members are on welfare, they fall below the income level that would require payment for service. Collection of fees has been difficult, and Council House has learned that persons referred whose income would require them to pay are apt to reject Council House, particularly since the financial status of the client must be learned on intake, without the candidate having had an opportunity to become involved or to build a relationship with anyone. This problem has been discussed with local officials of the county program who are sympathetic and are currently "intervening on behalf of the membership to help ease this alienation of some persons who badly need services."

Data were not available whereby one could translate the Council House budget into cost per contact, cost per case closed, cost per month, or any other basis that might permit comparison with other agencies offering comparable services. It did seem to us that a tremendous amount of service was being provided for the amount of money involved. One possibly acceptable index would be a comparison of the Council House budget with expenditures for state mental hospitals; Council House provides some degree of service to about 1200 per year, has approximately 500 active participants at any given time, participates actively in the vocational rehabilitation of a limited number, and does all this for the cost of keeping 32 people in a state hospital for a year.

Outcome

Council House has not done much formal outcome research other than to keep records of which of its members are rehospitalized. They report with justifiable pride that only five and a half percent of their membership require rehospitalization. Even granting that there is a self-selection factor influencing who comes to and uses Council House services, this remarkably low readmission rate is significant and offers compelling evidence of the value of the program. (The rate has dropped over the years from a high of twelve to fifteen percent to the present five and a half percent.)

In the final report submitted to the National Institute of Mental Health at the termination of the demonstration grant, Council House set forth a number of its findings that should be of interest and value to others considering establishing such programs.

• It is feasible to use volunteers to initiate, staff, and give policy direction to a community-based mental health agency.

• Volunteers who have acquired an understanding of mental illness will continue their work with mental patients in spite of occasional stories about attempted or actual violence by mentally ill persons.

• Under professional guidance ex-mental patients and persons still in mental hospitals can be screened for their suitability for participating in a community-based social support agency.

• Full-time professional guidance and supervision are required to conduct such a service.

• Ex-mental patients and some still hospitalized are capable of offering help to one another under guidance of professionals and volunteers.

• Many mental patients who are too ill to perform many normal social roles can maintain themselves in the community provided appropriate supportive services are rendered. If hospitalization becomes necessary, it usually can be done with the patient's voluntary assent and without breaking established community ties.

• Social agencies and private business firms can be encouraged to employ ex-mental patients on a volunteer, part-time, and full-time basis, provided an agency such as Council House is available to encourage them.

• A community-based mental health agency can exist with a membership that includes all races, ethnic groups, religions, and social classes.

• True psychiatric emergencies are rare, but when they do occur patients and their families are likely to find it difficult to reach people who can offer immediate help.

• A community mental health agency such as Council House can function well on a supportive counseling basis, provided intensive social casework and/or psychiatric consultation are available for special situations.

Plans for the future

Council House has evidently weathered the organizational and financial uncertainties that plagued it for many years, and one can believe that it will grow in importance and role in future years. If it is successful in establishing itself as the rehabilitation arm of ten community mental health centers, and in developing the necessary satellite facilities and staff that this would require, in rounding out its program and providing more intensive vocational services, the outlook for an expanded role and effectiveness seems bright.

Among the interesting specific projects that Council House now plans is the acquisition of a greenhouse which would provide continued employment for some of its more chronic and regressed members who do not seem to have much potential at present for ever getting into competitive work. A $50,000 grant from a local foundation has been given to Council House for such a purpose, and at the time this is written the agency continues its search for a suitable facility to buy.

The agency was honored in June 1970 by the Allegheny County United Mental Health Services with a special award.

VIII. Horizon House
Philadelphia

Origins

Horizon House came modestly into being in 1953 as the result of the efforts of a young woman who had been hospitalized for mental illness and a group of citizens that she enlisted in her campaign to create community support for people coming out of mental hospitals. The majority of this small group of citizens, who became the agency's first board of directors, were members of the Society of Friends, motivated by their concern for the plight of the mentally ill, and with very little professional or political connections.

During the first two years, the program had virtually no staff, and its activities were limited to social events held one evening per week. But this period was also marked by organizing efforts—to get chartered, to get publicity, to raise funds.

In 1956, the first director was hired, Irvin Rutman, a clinical psychologist who still holds the post. The resocialization program was extended to several evenings a week. Still, in those early years, efforts were "simple and modest." For the most part, Horizon House provided merely a place for the meetings—"a place to find some sense of security in an otherwise indifferent or alien community, and an opportunity to relearn basic social and interpersonal skills in an unthreatening setting."

At about this time, the City of Philadelphia became interested in Horizon House and provided money for some part-time staff; about a year afterward, the state began to provide grant-in-aid support. Since then, the program has grown steadily. Individual counseling services were added, daytime group meetings were begun, and a pilot vocational evaluation program was started. In 1961, a major grant to establish a comprehensive community-based service was received from SRS, and by 1966, when Horizon House won the Gold Award of the American Psychiatric Association's Hospital and Community Psychiatry Service, the agency's program consisted of *a*) social, vocational, recreational, and counseling services provided in a four-story town house in downtown

Philadelphia; *b*) an industrial workshop; *c*) a halfway residence for men who had been discharged from mental hospitals; and *d*) a specialized community residence, operated as an NIMH demonstration project, whose purpose was to serve as an alternate to hospitalization. Additional components, as described below, have been added since that time. Today Horizon House, the second oldest of the psychosocial rehabilitation centers, is one of the two largest in terms of facilities and program, and the largest in terms of staff.

Philosophy and purposes

In the early years, Horizon House attempted to provide support to people who had been hospitalized for mental illness, with no limit on length of service. About the time it began to acquire staff, a theoretical approach was developed emphasizing the program's intention to be a transitional facility, one that would provide support and impart skills to its members during a time of particular vulnerability. This transitional characteristic, with the movement upward and outward of clients, has never been fully achieved. "The philosophy has been well stated over the years," said Dr. Rutman, "but it never became fully implemented, despite the fact that the staff has heard it stated innumerable times." This stemmed to a large extent from the fact that the agency traditionally worked with all persons referred, no matter how severe their degree of chronicity or dependence. As a result, the staff was reluctant to limit or terminate services, recognizing that no other facility existed for such clients in the Philadelphia area.

At the time of our visit, Horizon House was about to move into an impressive new physical plant designed for its purposes, and concurrently with this change of locus was completing plans to implement a newly formulated philosophy of transitional service. Among the numerous staff members we interviewed, there was of course not a perfect consensus, and there was some concern about the future lot of many "long timers" who had come to be steadily dependent upon Horizon House without showing much promise of moving very far toward autonomous living. The new program did not intend to abandon this group, but rather was developing a special program to serve them, to take place at the original Pine Street house.

The new primary program has been well formulated. It was in large part the outgrowth of two weekend "retreats" made by the full staff, plus dozens of meetings of the supervisory staff. It had been presented to the members in a series of "town meetings" and through the monthly newsletter.

Because the new program is based on many years of experience, lengthy thought and deliberation, and a thorough knowledge of the literature and state-of-the-art of rehabilitation of the mentally ill, it seems useful to present Horizon House's own description.

1. The new Horizon House rehabilitation program seeks to establish a positive expectation on the part of both client and staff that will convey the following attitudes:

    A. Horizon House has available a combination of program components, and the skills needed to employ them, that will benefit the client significantly.

    B. In the rehabilitation process, the client is an active participant, who enters into his program willingly, whose viewpoints about his progress are valued, and who is prepared to make a commitment of time, effort, and motivation toward the successful completion of his program.

    C. Through this combination of mutual commitment and expectation, there will be generated a positive climate that should influence all interpersonal transactions throughout the agency.

2. The Horizon House rehabilitation program shall be limited in time to one year. Although this period is somewhat arbitrarily selected, it represents, based on experience, the best estimate of the maximum time that should be required to enable an individual to realize full benefits of the program.

3. The emphasis of Horizon House's efforts is on rehabilitation. It is no longer necessary for the agency to act as a *de facto* community mental health center, since operating centers now exist. Therefore, while we will continue to accept every client referred to us regardless of the severity of his disability, we will do so in the framework of the high-expectancy, one-year time limit noted above. If at the end of that period we have been unsuccessful in achieving our objectives, further arrangements for services for that individual — either at a community mental health center, or at the special Horizon House program designed for this purpose — will be made.

4. To help reinforce the client's commitment to the Horizon House program and the mutual feeling of expectation, all clients will be expected to pay a fee for service. We recognize, of course, that many of our members have extremely limited incomes, and for these members, particularly, fees will be clearly modest in amount. The principle, however, which should be clear, is that clients will be expected to make at least some payment in recognition of the value of the services they are receiving.

5. Horizon House views the rehabilitation program as sequential in

nature. By this is meant that the program progresses in a systematic direction of less to more complexity, less to more independence, and less to more activities preparatory to independent performance in society. Specifically, this is reflected in the fact that the program is separated into four phases, with Phase I representing programs designed for the lowest functioning level of clients and Phase IV for clients on the threshold of graduating from Horizon House. Within and between each of the phases, there is continuity of program activity. An individual leaves Phase I, for example, prepared to enter Phase II, and so forth.

6. To effect rehabilitation, the Horizon House program draws on a combination of five program modalities. These include educationally oriented programs; vocational training, work habituation, and counseling programs; group therapeutic programs; socio-recreational group activity programs; and supportive individual counseling programs. In this sense, Horizon House is attempting to create its own model (a combination model) rather than to rely primarily on a traditional model such as medical, social work, confrontational, etc.

7. To the fullest degree possible, every client participating in the Horizon House program will have a stipulated "roster" of program assignment, which will be developed jointly by staff and client. This program will be specified and known to all pertinent staff, insuring that clients will not get lost within the program.

8. Continuing evaluation of the client and of the effectiveness of the programs offered him is an integral feature of the new direction. Client evaluation and program evaluation have the same priority within the agency's framework as does the provision of direct services. It is only by systematic examination of the activities provided, their impact on the client, and his subsequent adjustment that we will be able to continue to improve the quality of our offerings.

Management and administration

A nonprofit corporation, Horizon House has a board of directors of nineteen members, consisting of mental health professionals, businessmen, educators, and laymen. The board meets monthly for a two-and-a-half-hour luncheon meeting, usually attended by twelve to fifteen members. Leadership comes from a youthful and enthusiastic nucleus. The board has program development, community affairs, and several other standing committees and assumes the broad policy-making responsibility for the organization. For many years there also existed a professional advisory committee whose contribution was limited mainly to lending professional prestige to Horizon House. In view of the inactive and now unnecessary function of this group, the agency recently decided to discontinue it.

The executive director is hired by the board and is responsible to it. He in turn acts as the staff's representative to the board, and vice versa. Customarily the executive director, the administrator, and the program director attend the monthly board meetings.

The organization table shows four components reporting to the executive director. One of these is the special NIMH-funded "alternatives to hospitalization" demonstration; another is the research department; the third is the administrator, who is responsible for business and fiscal matters and who supervises the bookkeeping and clerical staff. The fourth, with the greatest diversity of responsibility, is the program coordinator, who supervises the vocational, socialization, and group counseling activities that involve the bulk of the Horizon House membership, plus the long-established halfway house.

Physical facilities

The Horizon House program has been spread among several facilities and, by early 1970, had embraced its newest and largest additional physical plant. At the time of our visit, the "nerve center" of Horizon House was a four-story brownstone, known as the Pine Street Center, located in an anonymous downtown area of very good quality, near Rittenhouse Square and several leading hotels, amid antique and decorators' shops, good restaurants, etc. This rather ramshackle building had been the headquarters of the program since 1959. The administrative and staff offices, plus rooms for the daytime and evening social activities, were located there. The old house had obviously been put to good use, despite the fact that it was considerably run-down and in various respects not very well adapted to many of the activities carried on in it. It seemed to have an atmosphere which both staff and members valued, with an air of informality and friendly acceptance together with an obvious feeling of being busy.

Approximately half a mile away was the sheltered training workshop, comprising a floor of an industrial building located in the midst of a manufacturing and wholesale district. This facility, which will not be continued now that the new building is completed, was far from modern and seemed much like any number of other "lofts" used by small businesses located in large cities. It was, however, spacious and light.

About a mile from the Pine Street Center in another direction is "Horizon House West," the halfway house that for many years served only men, but has recently begun also to accept women.

At the time of our visit, Horizon House was only about two months from the date of taking occupancy of its very large and handsome new facility. It is located in Society Hill, a transitional neighborhood that seems well on the way to becoming an upper-middle-class residential section with many handsome Federal houses, which have been renovated; it is strongly reminiscent of the Georgetown section of Washington, D.C.

The new building occupies a large corner lot. It was built at a cost of about $815,000, of which approximately 65 percent came from the federal government in the form of a construction grant under the Community Mental Health Centers Act. Thus, Horizon House has, since our visit, joined New York's Fountain House as the second psychosocial rehabilitation center in the country to be housed in a facility constructed for its own purposes and use.

The modern three-story structure is light, airy, and spacious. It includes room for many kinds of group activities, for clerical training and contract sheltered workshops, food management and maintenance training, classrooms, and office space for both staff and students. Areas in which patient activities will take place occupy most of the space, with the size and number of staff accommodations kept to the necessary minimum.

The staff

With 67 full-time and seven part-time staff members as of the date of taking occupancy of its new physical plant, Horizon House is, in terms of staff size, the largest such facility in the United States. But a good number of these are assigned for the majority of the time to program components other than the new central facility at Society Hill. For example, there are two cadres totaling sixteen persons who are Horizon House employees but are assigned full time to provide services to each of two community mental health centers that contract aftercare and rehabilitation services from Horizon House. There are six who spend most of their time at the halfway house and six others who were assigned to Spruce House, the experimental halfway house, but have since been reassigned to the special program developed to serve the most regressed clients.

In terms of training, the Horizon House staff ranges from those who have the highest professional credentials for their respective disciplines to those who have no training whatever except that which Horizon House provided to them after they came to work. The director of the agency has a doctorate in clinical psychology, as does the program coordinator. The administrator holds a master's degree. The research director holds a doctoral degree in social psychology. There are seven social workers, six rehabilitation counselors, and two research associates trained at the master's level.

Much of the excitement and vitality of Horizon House seems specifically to stem from the particular fusion that it has successfully accomplished between trained and untrained staff. Some of the professionally trained people came to Horizon House because they were disaffected by "rigidities" of more traditional settings where they had been working. Others came on student placements, liked what they saw, and stayed on. Relatively few were actively recruited, simply because recruitment has rarely been necessary.

There seems to be an absence of concern with pathology, and instead an emphasis upon the everyday problems of the lives of the members. In this regard, Horizon House may be the best example the authors have seen of effective integration of untrained personnel with professionals. This is perhaps not so much "role blurring," such as we have seen in other types of facilities, as a realization that along with specialization of function—for example, most members have a trained caseworker to whom they are assigned—there are qualities of personality and values that professionals and untrained workers can combine to the members' benefit. We talked with "mental health workers" who supervise the members who have been placed in residential settings; they go so far as to intervene with "greedy landlords," help the members to bank and budget their money, escort members who seem to be deteriorating back to the clinics for adjustment of medication.

Several of the students with whom we talked expressed their initial concern, followed by a great awakening in the face of the Horizon House method of operating. They seemed uniformly to prefer Horizon House to their more formal previous placements. Many staff members do not have private offices, nor conduct many of the traditional kinds of interviews across desks; they dress casually; they see their members for "corridor consultations" about their problems. There was, all in all, a great feeling of vitality, common sense, and deep investment on the part of all the staff people that we interviewed.

Three attitudes in particular are valued highly by the staff and make themselves felt throughout the agency's orientation and programs. The first is an emphasis on openness and equality of relationship between the staff and clientele, in which the staff strives to relate to the members as people rather than patients and attempts to eliminate status differences as thoroughly as possible. The second deals with the staff's desire to

serve in an advocate rather than merely traditional professional relationship, as reflected in its willingness to initiate and follow through with
helpful actions—with other social agencies, employers, families, or neighbors, as needed—to facilitate the client's progress. The third is that Horizon House must involve itself thoroughly in the activities and concerns
of its community, and vice versa. The agency seeks opportunities to
bring the community into its program and facilities and is attempting to
extend its outreach so that more neighborhood groups and functions may
be centered around the agency.

Volunteers

Horizon House has never used volunteers extensively, mainly, it
appears, because the agency was started at the behest of former mental
patients rather than as a project of a service organization. Even so, the
extent of volunteer activity was greater in the agency's earlier years than
it is now. Presently about ten volunteers—college students, housewives,
and occasional professionals—help out in the socialization program,
mainly in the evenings. The Horizon House staff "have never made volunteer recruitment, training, and supervision a top priority, in relation
to other pressing demands on their time." But it is anticipated that
greater emphasis may be placed on the use of volunteers in the new
four-phase program, particularly on recruiting volunteers "from the
client's community." Several neighbors of the new Society Hill facility
had already signed up for volunteer service even before the new building was occupied.

Clientele

Eligibility. For the socialization activities and the vocational program,
there is no eligibility requirement except that the applicant have a psychiatric history and that he not behave in a severely disruptive way.
The vast majority of Horizon House members, more than ninety percent, have been hospitalized for psychiatric reasons, and all of the rest
have been or still are outpatients. Less than one percent of applicants
are refused service on the grounds of being too ill. Many of those who
become members have had alcoholism and drug abuse problems. "If
these are identified as the primary presenting symptom," we were told,
"we might think twice before accepting them; but generally this has not
been a problem, either because such people haven't found their way to
Horizon House or because we are not sensitized to the question."
    More rigorous screening takes place for persons seeking to enter the
halfway house program. Neither the halfway house nor the experimental

Spruce Street residence will accept persons with primary diagnosis of addiction, those with substantial physical impairments, or "aggressive overt homosexuals."

Age. The substantial majority of people who become Horizon House members are between 21 and 50—specifically, 76 percent of the men and 67 percent of the women. There is a putative lower age limit of 18, but the program sometimes accepts 16- and 17-year-olds; clients under 21 constitute 13 percent of the men and 11 percent of the women. Very few members are over 60—only about one percent each of men and women.

Sex. Almost two thirds of the members (64 percent) are men.

Race. Twenty-two percent of the members are Negroes. This contrasts with about 40 percent of the patients being discharged from the state hospitals that serve Philadelphia, and with about 35 percent of the city's general population.

Residential status. More than a third of the members (36 percent) are living with their parents; 14 percent are living alone; ten percent are living with their wives or husbands and/or children; and 40 percent are living in other kinds of arrangements, including those still living in hospitals and in the agency's own halfway house.

Employment status. The modal group of both men and women members are unemployed during most of their active association with Horizon House (78 percent of the total group). The next largest group is those who are competitively employed full time, consisting of 16 percent of the members. The remaining few are either in part-time competitive employment or in full-time work in some sheltered setting.

Diagnosis. Horizon House never receives information on diagnosis for about one fifth (21 percent) of its members. Of the rest, by far the largest group is persons who have been diagnosed as schizophrenic (65 percent), followed by personality disorders (18 percent), neurotic disorders (eight percent), organic brain syndromes (five percent), depressive reactions (four percent), and mental deficiency (one percent).

The intake process

Referrals. Horizon House accepts referrals from virtually any source. The largest group, twenty percent, is those who either come in on their own or are referred by relatives or friends. Next come referrals from state hospitals (17 percent), community mental health centers (16 percent), general hospital psychiatric services (13 percent). The welfare department refers six percent; psychiatrists in private practice, five percent; a rehabilitation facility for the mentally ill and retarded, four percent; a Veterans Administration hospital, a private mental hospital, and the state vocational rehabilitation agency, three percent each. Horizon House does not know the referral source for about ten percent of its members.

T HE INTAKE PROCESS has been modified repeatedly over the years, "partly in an effort to improve internal efficiency and partly as the result of such external demands as state requirements." Nonetheless, at all times there has been an open-door policy, whereunder virtually all psychiatrically disabled adults have been eligible for membership.

At the time of our visit, under the old program, prospective members were first seen in a casework interview designed to acquaint them with the content of the program and to give them an opportunity to decide whether or not they wish to attend. At this point, for purposes of the state's statistical system, they are counted as having been served. Those who return—about 65 percent—enter an orientation group run by the social group workers. If the new member is sponsored by the Bureau of Vocational Rehabilitation, he will then be evaluated and tested according to that agency's requirements. Once the patient is a Horizon House member, he is eligible for the full services of the agency.

As part of the implementation of the new four-phase program, all current members of Horizon House have been re-evaluated, meeting two at a time with a three-person staff group representing social group work, social casework, and vocational counseling. Following this "staffing," each is assigned to his indicated level in the four-step program.

New members coming in to the program are similarly assessed. Intake for new members includes an interview with a psychiatrist and continues with interviews with the group worker, caseworker, and vocational counselor. When the member begins in one of the training workshops (Phase II), he is given the prescribed Bureau of Vocational Rehabilitation battery of standardized tests. Thus, the principal differences between the old and the new intake process are that the new one adds an assessment by a psychiatrist, requires the testing program for all new members rather than simply those being accepted for Vocational Rehabilitation sponsorship, and establishes a climate of mutuality of program decision-making between staff and member.

The new process incorporates an initial two-week evaluation and orientation period, during which the client has an opportunity to meet representatives of the various group activities and the vocational departments and fellow clients, and to observe the program. Following this evaluation period, the new member and various staff members meet together to appraise his needs and readiness; at this time, a statement of his commitment to the program is sought. Thus, he and the staff agree on a schedule of particular program activities, and he is prepared to begin participation as a full-fledged member the following week. He may enter the program at any of the four phases, depending upon his particular situation.

Dropouts. In the old program membership status was permanent, and the only termination resulting from nonparticipation was a statistical one, to satisfy the requirements of the state; specifically, any person who had not been active in any program element at all for a period of three months was "statistically terminated," but was still welcome to return at any time he wished. For the new program, envisioning a time limit of approximately one year, the process by which members will be terminated has not been fully formulated.

Horizon House has attempted over the years to reactivate members who dropped out before the staff felt they had received maximum benefit from the program. The effort was characterized as "far from systematic." In a particularly interesting research study, a group of dropouts were contacted, some by telephone, others by home visits. It was found that a single such contact resulted in 38 percent of the dropouts returning to active status. The rate of reactivation was approximately the same for the two different methods of approach.

Under the new system Horizon House has developed a procedure for follow-up of dropouts, as well as graduates, that is more thorough and systematic. All dropouts from the first two phases of the program are contacted by their caseworker-coordinator at least once a week for four consecutive weeks, and again one month later. Thereafter a random sample will be followed for information purposes by a special follow-up person. If a client drops out from Phase III or Phase IV, he is contacted weekly for eight weeks, and again a random sample will be followed on a monthly basis by the special follow-up worker. Horizon House believes that this procedure will result in returning many dropouts, perhaps the majority, to the program. Graduates are also followed up to determine their status in the community.

The program, in general

During 1969 Horizon House had approximately 1200 clients; but it must be remembered that under the statistical reporting system used to satisfy state requirements, any person who so much as comes in for an initial interview is counted as having been served. It is more instructive, therefore, to consider the caseload for a particular month. In October

1969, a rather slow month, 36 new members completed the intake process. There were 240 different persons who received one degree or another of service during the month. Seventy-four of these attended the evening program, an average of three times each. There were 667 individual interviews with 235 different members, an average of just under three each; these included interviews conducted by social case and group workers, psychiatric interviews, vocational counseling, testing, and evaluation. There were 1353 "attendances" at 183 group sessions, an average of about seven persons per group. These included social and vocational counseling, special interest and socialization groups, volunteer programs, and adult education classes. There were 83 "collateral contacts" on behalf of 42 clients, and there were five home visits.

During this same month, 63 people spent some time working in the sheltered workshop, and 18 were referred to other vocational training programs or for regular employment. Ten individuals were placed in employment directly through Horizon House efforts, and three others indirectly.

In the field units set up to serve the Jefferson and Pennsylvania Hospital Community Mental Health Centers, a total of 305 different clients were served, as follows: 208 persons were seen in 370 individual counseling interviews; 61 were seen in 110 group counseling sessions; there were 279 collateral contacts on behalf of 116 members; and 168 home visits were made to 83 members.

We referred to the month in which 240 members were served as a slow one. During the first nine months of 1969, the number of persons served per month ranged from a low of 217 to a high of 481. The pattern is irregular, a high or low month often being followed by the opposite. The staff were not certain why this large fluctuation. In any case, the mean number of persons served during those nine months was 343 per month in Horizon House programs and 228 through the field units assigned to the mental health center catchment areas.

The four-phase program

It seems pointless to describe the details of the Horizon House program as it operated until the beginning of 1970, since the new four-phase program not only vastly changes the agency's approach to service but also incorporates the principles that were learned from the dozen preceding years of program experimentation and refinement. Consequently, despite its newness, we shall describe the new program, in the belief that it may represent as sophisticated an approach to rehabilitating the mentally ill as has been developed thus far. The outlines for the new program resemble a well-prepared educational curriculum, to a much larger extent than anything the authors had seen previously in the mental health field. The course outlines not only include the goals of the particular course, the content week by week, and the materials needed, but also identify the behavioral outcome criteria that will be used to determine whether or not a given client has passed the course.

It must be emphasized that despite the time-limited and firmly programmed approach, there has been some leeway built into the program. Specifically, as we have mentioned, a client need not start at Phase I, but may ostensibly begin even at Phase IV if he seems ready for it; similarly, a person who does not successfully complete Phase I the first time through but still seems to possess rehabilitation potential may repeat the phase or some particular course or courses from it.

Phase I. Phase I emphasizes basic remedial training in the fundamentals of everyday living and is intended for the most seriously regressed and chronic applicants. This three-month phase calls for participation in any or all of three educational programs—home management, personal hygiene, and community resources. Each consists of two five-week units of increasing complexity; thus, a complete Phase I home management course would continue for ten weeks. Within the thirteen-week period allocated to the phase, there is a latitude of three weeks for any member to repeat any part of the coursework that he may not have been able to pass.

In addition to participation in one, two, or three of the formal courses, the member is also scheduled for ten hours a week of combined morning work program and prevocational orientation and is assigned to group counseling sessions that meet four hours per week. This open-end but continuing group, led by a staff counselor and described as using a "confrontational approach," continues into and through Phase II, under the same leadership. (The agency displays no concern or diffidence about conducting group therapy activities, which it labels as such. The staff sees the strengthening of clients' personal and emotional awareness as an essential aspect of their total rehabilitation program, without which the various educational and vocational activities would be of limited value.)

An additional activity which completes the content of Phase I is postintake counseling, either individual or in very small groups, provided by the particular caseworker or counselor who conducts the initial intake interview. This exposure, often quite informal in nature, is intended to orient the new member to the agency, to allow an opportunity to answer any questions, and to maintain close touch with his progress.

The entire content of Phase I calls for up to 25 hours a week of the client's participation.

Phase II. The second phase is designed to introduce the new member to a combination of social and vocational activities, augmented by group counseling. The classroom sequences are continued, but on a less intense and time-consuming basis. To take up this time, the member is assigned three hours each day to work in one of the workshop training programs. He spends his mornings there and his afternoons in classes. The group counseling continues.

Phase III. In this phase the member spends the bulk of his time, about six hours a day, in one of the vocational training workshops, which provide industrial, clerical, maintenance, and food management training, all within the new facility. As the coursework is completed, the first group counseling sequence is supplanted by a vocationally oriented group counseling program led by staff from the vocational department. Phase III thus provides about thirty hours per week of workshop assignment plus four hours a week of group counseling, plus individual job counseling and preparation.

Phase IV. While workshop assignments continue, the amount of time is reduced in order to allow the member to look for work. Group counseling is intensified to a daily basis and centers on job-seeking and job-holding behavior. Practice job interviews and temporary job tryouts are arranged with cooperating employers. If the individual finds employment, he will be followed by his counselor to keep check on his job adjustment.

Educational programs. The four phases can be supplemented when indicated with one of two levels of formal education. One is a "literacy" program dealing with basic language and arithmetic competence. The second is a program that prepares the individual to pass an examination that will give him a certificate equivalent to a high school diploma. These programs, which take place four daytime periods and two evenings a week, are provided at Horizon House in cooperation with the Philadelphia Board of Education.

Coordination of responsibility. The intake worker who guides the new member into the program retains responsibility for coordinating his program during Phases I and II, in part by conducting the postintake sessions. In Phases III and IV coordination of program becomes the responsibility of the vocational department; thus, new members entering the program at Phase III or IV are directly assigned to a vocational or rehabilitation counselor who serves as coordinator.

A curriculum. Because of the inventive nature of the formal curricula for this program, it seems useful to give as an example the description of a particular course from Phase I.

Name of course: Home Management I
> (housecleaning—kitchen,   Number of weeks: 5
> bedroom, and bath)   Number of times per week: 3

Goals of course
> 1. To know rudiments of housecleaning.
> 2. To know basic household safety measures.
> 3. To know some fundamentals of decorating, repairs, and renovations (use of tools, use of needle and thread).

Exit test criteria
> 1. Use appropriate equipment to clean an area of kitchen, bath, and living room (lounge).
> 2. Role play in closet and kitchen area, storage of cleansers, medicines, matches, hot foods, etc.
> 3. Identify and use tools, needle and thread.

Course content (by week with extra options)

> *Week one*
>> Introduce and explain efficient use of basic tools (e.g., brooms, mops, sweepers, rags, dusters, etc.).
>> Introduce and explain various soaps, detergents, cleansers, how to read instructions, uses of various materials.

> *Week two*
>> Members of class practice use of implements and materials. Also practice reading and explaining instructions.
>> Explain use of containers and preservation of leftovers. Present containers that may be kept for later use (e.g., margarine tubs, etc.).

> *Week three*
>> Show use of materials like wax paper, Saran wrap, tin foil. Demonstrate wrapping.
>> Sanitary measures re garbage disposal, tins and bottles. Rules about not keeping garbage around, etc.

> *Week four*
>> Learn bed-making.
>> Present basic tools—hammer, screwdriver, pliers, nails, screws, nuts. Show their use (primarily for men, but females, too).

> *Week five*
>> Present basic tools of sewing and repairs (e.g., needle, thread,

buttons, etc.). Show their use (primarily for females, but men, too).

Practice these skills.

Materials needed

Brooms, mops, sweepers, dust cloths, various cleansers, few patent medicines and disinfectants; bed, bed clothing (sheets, etc.).

Addenda

1. Use of more complex instruments (e.g., vacuum cleaner, sewing machine, etc.).
2. Learn some specific basic repairs such as weak chair leg, etc.
3. Learn minor electrical repairs and safety measures, plugs, sockets, wire splice, etc.

Medication and psychiatric services

Dr. Rutman expresses the belief that the Horizon House program could not have progressed as extensively or as rapidly if psychoactive medications had not become available, and he relates the timing of the program's development to the emergence of the major tranquilizers. Thus, despite its relearning-styled approach, Horizon House nonetheless recognizes the contribution that medication makes to the stabilization of its members. It does not, however, impose a requirement to have a therapist as a precondition for acceptance into the program. In practice, most of the members do have a psychiatrist or other physician at the time they apply. "If they don't, and seem to require such help, our staff make the necessary arrangements," Dr. Rutman told us.

For about six years, until 1968, the program's part-time psychiatric consultant was Dr. James Harris, who continues as a member of the board of directors. He attended to the medication needs of the members and collaborated with Dr. Rutman in shaping the growth of the program.

Dr. Harris told us that "as time went on I used less and less symptomatic psychiatry and more and more an instrumental approach." He said that he learned in interviewing Horizon House clients that he should be more concerned with whether the client could attend the program for five consecutive days than with whether he was schizophrenic or suffering from a behavior disorder. He expressed the view that while diagnosis can often be helpful in understanding a client it is often misused. He saw the psychiatric consultant as having three major contributions to a program such as Horizon House; the first was in responding to suicide attempts, supervising medication in emergency cases, and arranging hospitalization when the need arose. The second was as a resource to other staff, especially those with limited background in the field. The third was in dealing with the outside psychiatric community, by facilitating relationships and referrals and interpreting the agency to the psychiatric community.

Involvement of families

As with the other centers, Horizon House has little focus on the family—"because family ties are often nonexistent, weak, or unsatisfactory." The occasional involvement of relatives happens for the most part with younger clients.

The satellite programs affiliated with the Jefferson and Pennsylvania Hospital Community Mental Health Centers do make a great many home visits; in a month late in 1969 the Jefferson Unit, for example, made 168. Some of these involve families, but many do not, since quite a lot of members do not live with their families.

Agency and community relationships

The major Horizon House relationship with an official agency is presently that with the Philadelphia County Office of Mental Health and Retardation, which contracts with Horizon House to provide aftercare and rehabilitation services and, in turn, provides a large portion of its budget. A psychiatric social worker assigned by the county office to Horizon House spends a large part of her time there conferring with various members of the staff. She expressed the view that rehabilitation services of this nature may well not be needed within each mental health center catchment area but rather can be regionalized to serve several centers.

Another important agency relationship is with the Bureau of Vocational Rehabilitation. A BVR counselor works full time directly at Horizon House and has a fairly free hand in making decisions about accepting or rejecting members applying for BVR support. Because of limited funds, it appears probable that under the new program BVR will be able to support clients only when they have reached Phase II. Under the old program, the counselor was authorized to accept clients on her own judgment, without testing, for a period of twenty weeks and then could extend the period of service for as much as twenty weeks longer if she saw definite progress and was persuaded that additional time would accomplish some particular objective.

We have mentioned the contractual arrangements with Jefferson and Pennsylvania Hospital Community Mental Health Centers, under which Horizon House provides aftercare and rehabilitation components for these centers. The staff members assigned to these responsibilities are members of the Horizon House staff, but they are included in the federal staffing grants of the two centers.

Horizon House has been a financially participating member of the United Fund since 1965.

"In addition to our formal relationships," Dr. Rutman told us, "we have developed informal relationships with many hospitals, social agencies, and mental health agencies. We provide aftercare and rehabilitation services, although without a formal agreement, to any suitable applicant coming from any of the other mental health center catchment areas; while we plan to formalize these arrangements, there probably will not be any additional federal funds as a result of our doing so. We also have friendly and constructive albeit informal relationships with the five state hospitals in and around Philadelphia, two Veterans Administration hospitals, three sheltered workshops, and the mental health association, among others."

One of the detached mental health workers described setting up socialization centers at two Methodist churches, one in a mainly black neighborhood, the other in an Italian neighborhood. The role of the churches is principally limited to providing the premises for the program run by Horizon House "to give our members a chance to get out of their rooming houses and their empty lives, to come and have coffee and doughnuts, things to read, games to play, and fun."

Another staff member described his efforts in soliciting from nonprofit agencies volunteer work for the Horizon House members to do as part of the prevocational program. He also sends some of these same members to these agencies to do volunteer work on their own premises. Some agencies provide bus fare and lunch money and a few pay a small salary.

The vocational department supervisor must deal with a variety of businesses in order to keep an adequate workload for the workshops, but by and large this has been no problem "since we perform a service for them better than they could do it themselves." For example, the workshop does packaging jobs which would require more space and temporary help than the business firms can manage. The workshop supervisor goes out and obtains contracts, does a work study on them, and then prices them. Despite these mutually supportive relationships with employers, there have been problems in the past. One large department store, for example, gave Horizon House a "block placement," taking ten members in shipping and receiving jobs, on the clerical staff, and so on. These were designed as temporary work-experience placements, intended to last three months only. The store insisted, however, on holding on to persons initially placed rather than letting the job serve as a transitional experience, and consequently the arrangement was terminated.

The most serious and substantially the only significant conflict that Horizon House has had with its neighbors concerned the experimental Spruce House program. From the outset there was organized opposition from a neighborhood civic organization. Spruce House applied for a zoning variance but was turned down. It then appealed the ruling; by that time the program had been in existence for most of the four-year demonstration period for which it was funded, and Horizon House gave up any further efforts to maintain the program.

"Although we are now fairly well known, we are still concerned about community understanding and acceptance," Dr. Rutman told us. "Thus, in preparing to move into our new facility, we formed a staff committee that actively informed the surrounding community about our impending move. The committee sent staff, students, and one of our members to stores and homes in the immediate vicinity, distributed brochures and met with various community leaders. The general reception was favorable. Shortly after we occupied the new building we started a series of 'open houses' for neighbors, educators, and mental health professionals."

Training

The principal formal training provided by Horizon House is in the form of field placement for students of graduate schools of social work and rehabilitation counseling. At the time of our visit there were two second-year students from Bryn Mawr, two others from Antioch, and one each from the Pennsylvania State and Temple University rehabilitation counselor training programs.

One Bryn Mawr student described her experience at Horizon House as "considerably different from and more exciting than" what she experienced in other agencies which she had previously been assigned to. Through the entire second year of her master's program, she spends three days a week doing intake interviews, handling a continuing individual casework load of eight patients, and sitting in on some of the group sessions. She said that Horizon House is much less structured than her other casework placements.

The Antioch students spend their days at the principal facility and sleep at the halfway house. It appeared that they involve themselves flexibly and at their own pace, engaging with patients in ways they feel they can comfortably handle.

About twenty undergraduates from Philadelphia Community College and Temple University spend about six hours per week each at Horizon

House as part of their work toward a degree in social welfare and community mental health. They help in the vocational and group work departments in various counseling, testing, and teaching program functions.

Financing and fees

Horizon House derives its income from a variety of public and private sources. The financial picture during the recent past has been one of tremendous change and expansion. For example, the budget in 1968-69 was $458,000 and the anticipated budget for 1969-70 was $690,000. Most of this increase was accounted for by the implementation in Philadelphia of the new county-administered mental health and retardation program whereunder Horizon House would receive about $430,000 to provide aftercare, rehabilitation, and group living services. The following breakdown illustrates how drastically the funding status changed in a single year. (Neither year's figures include funds received from NIMH in support of the Spruce House demonstration project.)

	1968-69		1969-70	
	Amount	*Percent*	*Amount*	*Percent*
Bureau of Vocational Rehabilitation	$108,000	*24*	$120,000	*17*
State program funding (grant-in-aid)	168,000	*37*		
Federal staffing grant	125,000	*27*	90,000	*13*
United Fund	30,000	*7*	30,000	*4*
Workshop contracts	20,000	*4*	20,000	*3*
City of Philadelphia	5,000	*1*		
County of Philadelphia (MH-MR program)			430,000	*62*

Future financing seems unclear, because of the prospects that the county will change over from program budgeting to fee-for-service. But, in general, this well-regarded program seems to have favorable financial prospects, despite uncertainties caused by year-to-year fluctuations in the amount of state funds available to be earmarked for Horizon House by the county administrator's office and the Bureau of Vocational Rehabilitation. Funds have been remarkably slow in being allocated, and in some cases as much as a year has elapsed. This not only keeps Horizon House and a host of other mental health programs in the dark about how much money they will eventually have to spend, but also requires that they constantly juggle monies from one pocket to another. At the time of our visit in November, the agency had not received any funds from the state or county for the first five months of the fiscal year.

Horizon House has rarely charged fees of its members, except at the halfway house, where, in most cases, the fees were paid by a living allowance from the Bureau of Vocational Rehabilitation.

Outcome and other research

Horizon House has had a research department since 1962, headed up from the outset by a social psychologist who at present has a staff of five. The program is described as consisting of three types of efforts: *a*) evaluative studies that examine the effectiveness of specific procedures and programs, including follow-up studies; *b*) controlled experiments aimed at program improvement; and *c*) investigations concerned with uncovering causal relationships between disability factors, program content, and subsequent adjustment.

One major study carried out during 1963-65 followed up two hundred members who were accepted as clients by the Bureau of Vocational Rehabilitation. They were followed over an eighteen-month period. Their rehospitalization rate was about thirty percent within one year, as contrasted with about forty percent for those not participating in post-hospital programs. The research director described the outcome as "generally unsatisfactory in terms of disclosing predictors." Test batteries were used, but it was not possible to predict from them who would do well and who would not.

Another major research effort was carried out as part of the Spruce House demonstration program. From a population all evaluated as requiring hospitalization, individuals were randomly assigned to the state hospital, to Spruce House, and to several small general hospitals. The results were still being analyzed at the time of our visit, but preliminary findings indicated that those who went into the halfway house rather than the hospital did at least as well in all respects as those who were hospitalized, and in some respects better.

Other research efforts have involved an experiment intended to reduce absenteeism from the workshop by experimental manipulations based on cognitive dissonance theory which showed that, contrary to what ordinarily might be expected, minimal amounts of reward given to reinforce promptness and steady attendance resulted in maintaining such sought-after behavior more effectively than did the giving of greater rewards. Another experiment already described attempted to reactivate members who had dropped out of the program.

The research staff have more adequate facilities at the new physical plant, and indeed describe the new facility as equivalent to a "laboratory" in which to carry out a number of studies, including a more comprehensive study of all clients, both those who drop out against staff advice and those who "graduate." The new follow-up system will involve service contact for a limited period—two months for dropouts and six months for graduates, with follow-up over a longer period on a random sample of both groups.

The goals and particulars of the evaluation program as it will be carried out in the new facility have been set forth, and in view of the experience of this research department over the years, it may be useful to indicate them here.

Goals of Evaluation

A. To establish a continuous, coordinated system of information feedback that would permit the constant monitoring of each client's progress throughout every phase of his rehabilitation program. In other words, it should be possible to know at any time *where* the client is, how long he has been there, how long he may remain in any phase, etc.

B. To provide the constant feedback of data that would permit the eventual development of objective criteria for initial program assignment, for determining promotions and failures, and for guiding the clients' total movement through the program. In short, these indices should provide an ongoing chart of *how* the client is doing.

C. To ascertain the relevance or relationship of client performance from one phase of the program to another and, most importantly, the relevance to postprogram follow-up criteria, such as job success. The effort here is to construct courses with demonstrated internal and external validity, and so eventually to establish predictors. This, of course, also means paying attention to flunk-outs and failures, and necessitates a thorough postprogram follow-up of all clients.

D. To offer the opportunity for systematic experimentation that would allow for innovation and change in course content, methods of teaching, etc., and that would result in the feedback of data to assess the effectiveness of such experiments.

E. Measurements will have to be tailored to the particular goals of each course, which will mean spelling out the exact goals of each course, and then devising methods for determining whether these goals have been met—both for exempting a client from a particular course and for setting minimal standards for passing a course.

F. Measurements should be as objective as possible.

Plans for the future

We have described in some detail the new program of Horizon House, designed after lengthy soul-searching about how to improve the quality of service to clients, and intended to yield a more successful outcome in terms of preventing rehospitalization and enabling clients to achieve and maintain employment and to lead more satisfying lives in the community. It may be useful to set forth some of the objectives of the program as they were perceived by Horizon House and described to us by Dr. Rutman.

• We felt a need to reduce a kind of laissez-faire approach, thereby reducing the chance that members will get "lost" within Horizon House. This involved placing a higher expectancy upon them, with the result of strengthening their commitment and their sense of self-responsibility.

• We needed a more systematic follow-up of clients, one which would alert us to those who were "stalled" in one or another phase of the program. Related to this was the need to formulate more certain criteria regarding the process of terminating a member and of assessing his community adjustment.

• Because of the need for a greater range and variety of sheltered workshop training activities, and a need to establish more and better relationships with employers for individuals as well as group placements, we will exert more effort in recruiting more stimulating workshop contracts and job placements—jobs that are more varied in content and better paying. This will include new methods of obtaining job orders, more extensive training in office and industrial skills, and basic experimentation on the work behavior of the psychiatric client.

• In the social arena, we realize the need for greater effort to involve ourselves in social programs in the community that cater to the general population, giving our clients exposure to them while they are still in our program and thereby preparing them to function better in normative social activities after they leave us.

• Perhaps most important is the need for a greater variety of suitable residential possibilities. Our own halfway house has only partially met the demand. We will try to recruit pleasant boardinghouse placements and reasonably priced rooms and apartments. We need to educate land lords better. Some of our clients could certainly benefit from long-term independently run lodges. The housing situation in Philadelphia for the former mental patient has been so poor that one can understand why many of our members find even a state hospital more homelike than what has been available to them.

IX. Thresholds
Chicago

Origins

Thresholds is a comprehensive, well-organized, energetic psychosocial rehabilitation center that was established in 1958 as a project of the Chicago chapter of the National Council of Jewish Women. The program started out with operating funds available from a demonstration grant from the National Institute of Mental Health, with the stated original purpose of helping people who had been mentally ill to "maintain the gains" made during the period of hospitalization. This effort centered entirely upon providing socialization experiences, such as conversation groups and card games, in the belief that a relatively short period of time "in an accepting supportive social environment would be sufficient to help the member regain the confidence he needed to return to the community."

The program continued in this vein for approximately four years. The lack of emphasis on vocational service was not the result of a lack of understanding that former mental patients may need such help, but rather because a variety of specialized vocational agencies were already available in the Chicago area and appeared to be providing appropriate service. But with time, Thresholds came to realize that many of the people who became its members were unable to use, at least initially, such well-developed agencies as the Goodwill Industries and the Jewish Vocational Service. This inability "lay in the fact that these patients needed a more comprehensive involvement on the part of the treatment agency than was possible in a primarily vocational agency. These patients were not, by and large, ready to enter the employment market on a full-time competitive basis, and in many instances were not ready to plan realistically with the vocational counselors around part-time or sheltered employment possibilities."

Consequently, in 1963, Thresholds revised its program to incorporate a variety of prevocational and vocational services which are described below. The research and program development was largely sponsored by what is now the Social and Rehabilitation Service. The awareness that

118

led to this change is important to the planning and operation of a psycho-social program whose clientele consists largely of people who have been patients in state mental hospitals, with a diagnosis of schizophrenia.

> Thresholds [was] serving most actively a group of individuals who can be considered to have failed in solving three of the major tasks of adulthood: *a*) they have failed to establish their independence from their parental families; *b*) they have failed to establish social relation-ships with their peers that could have resulted in marriage and a family of their own; *c*) they have failed to become self-supporting. . . .

> It became clear that the agency needed to provide *learning*, not *re-learning*, experiences for the members; that the agency was a step *towards* the community and adjustment therein, not a step *back* to a previous adjustment in the community. The original vision of Thresh-olds as aiding the posthospital patient to regain skills with which his illness had interfered, and rebuilding confidence and self-esteem, was found to be a service that only a small part of the agency's total pop-ulation needed. Programs were needed that could help the typical Thresholds member to acquire the social and emotional skills which he had never mastered.

In accordance with the original plan the sponsorship and financial support of the National Council of Jewish Women was phased out and a nonsectarian, community-wide board of directors was initiated. The agency has been independent since 1963.

Philosophy and purposes

Thresholds views itself as attempting to fill a major gap in mental illness services: as drug therapy and intensive-treatment hospital pro-grams have reduced the need for long-term hospitalization, with patients being returned in large numbers to the community, there are many who cannot resume work or return to their families without additional and specialized help of a kind often not provided by the hospitals. This is particularly true, in Thresholds' view, for chronic schizophrenic patients whose acute episode of illness may be over but who remain "basically schizophrenic, with a somewhat tenuous hold on reality and serious distortions in ability to relate to other people." If such a person is returned to the same environment that he left in order to enter the hospital, with the same inadequate defenses as before the acute phase of illness, and with his confidence in his ability to cope with life's problems shaken by the experience of hospitalization, then he may very likely end up in the hospital again unless special support resources and learning/training experiences are available to him.

Several components of program are considered essential. These include the opportunity for positive relationships with significant others; an expectation that appropriate adjustment is possible; and the rehearsal and improvement of social behavior which, in turn, act to upgrade his self-esteem and reduce his sense of alienation.

The assistant director put it in this way:

> Part of the illness and part of the problem is that the schizophrenic acts in ways that are unacceptable to society. Society in turn rejects the schizophrenic. Thus a cycle is set up. His being rejected further exacerbates the problem. But if at one point or another one can interrupt and help him to learn to behave appropriately in given social situations and relationships, then society will learn to accept him and he can learn to function. I've had very sick people who were hostile and delusional, who learned to keep their mouths shut about their illness and their delusions, who learned to walk down the street wearing a business shirt and a tie instead of some bizarre costume, who learned to work from nine to five and control their symptomatology. That's not to say that they're well or cured, but that they've learned to exist in society, and to find acceptance. Thus, you cut into a debilitating cycle, reverse it, and make it a habilitating cycle.

The director of Thresholds, Jerry Dincin, a social worker, more briefly describes the Thresholds recipe: *a*) a series of opportunities, *b*) high expectations, *c*) relationships with healthy people, *d*) psychiatric backup as needed, and *e*) emphasis on residual health of the individual. Mr. Dincin acknowledges that he does not know how the change is effected but believes that the member, by getting a new role, gets a new self-image. He feels that success experience is essential to the process.

In translation into a program, this philosophy comes down to the brass tacks of everyday living. People are taught how to enter rooms, to use the telephone, to work, to relate to supervision, to comb their hair, not to laugh too loudly in public places—in short, the many things that people who have been long institutionalized are likely to be awkward or bizarre about as the result of having lost touch with the reality of normative expectations.

The philosophy of the program was stated by a vocational counselor as one of "unlearning the behavior of illness." That is to say, if illness can be learned, it can also be unlearned. This fairly basic social-educational model seems to prevail among the Thresholds staff, and by emphasizing appropriate behavior, the staff hopes to help in breaking the deviance-rejection-deviance cycle.

In a "welcoming letter" prepared by Mr. Dincin for new members, Thresholds is described as a place to resume vocational responsibilities and to renew social life. It is also a place to share problems and successes, not only with a staff of professional social workers, but also with fellow members who may be experiencing similar problems and successes. Thresholds, in other words, is a place to learn, a place to change.

Rehabilitation is the goal of Thresholds' program and independence is its keynote. Through a variety of programs tailored to meet the unique needs of each member, Thresholds assists people in returning to the community with the ability and the confidence to control their own lives. Vocationally, members prepare for re-entry into the employment world by participating in Thresholds' extensive work program. Socially, through group activities designed to help people learn or renew skills needed in natural social relationships. In addition, Thresholds focuses on the various aspects of independent living: handling isolation, financial security, emotional rewards, etc. Finally, Thresholds counsels members in the very important areas of coping with symptoms, illness, and medication.

As its name implies, Thresholds is a place of transition. Once a person is accepted for membership, his transition from the hospital to the community will depend greatly upon how he chooses to utilize Thresholds. His attitude toward his year at Thresholds could spell the difference between rehabilitation and regression. And while it is true that the fear of change is very real and very great for many people, the rewards of change are greater and more satisfying. Ask any of the people who are participating in Thresholds' program, or who have graduated from Thresholds. . . .

Mr. Dincin believes that members should be eased into the community, particularly with respect to jobs. "I believe that psychiatric patients should by and large be started slowly, a few hours a week, and worked up to a forty-hour-a-week job. The rare person who needs a full-time job and seems ready for it, we send to the state employment service. But those who need part-time jobs we place in our program."

When asked whether the Thresholds program could be successfully duplicated within the context of a state hospital, one staff member said that it could not.

I don't think what we are doing could be successfully done even by an enlightened hospital, because there is still the tradition of custodialism, the large numbers of patients, the isolation. Real rehabilitation must be community-based.

Management and administration

As a voluntary nonprofit social agency, Thresholds is governed ultimately by a board of directors with an authorized strength of thirty. There were 28 members as of the time of our visit. There has been considerable continuity in membership, and there are still a few board members from the days when the agency operated as an activity of the National Council of Jewish Women.

The board is required to meet a minimum of eleven times per year. Attendance averages between fifteen and twenty. Most of the work is parceled out to an active group of committees, most of them administrative in nature, such as the budget and the nominating committees. There are also some "program" committees concerned, for example, with the various satellite programs.

Various staff members are directly assigned to board committees. For example, an employment opportunities committee includes two of the staff in its membership.

The members of the board are, in general, "representative." There are members chosen for their capabilities at raising funds, others for their professional background, and, more recently, some "community people" more representative of the socioeconomic group served by Thresholds.

There is a rather definite stricture against using board members as volunteers. This was tried at one time and led to problems. "It's very difficult for the staff, and particularly the director," Mr. Dincin said, "to relate to a single person who at one time is a volunteer, a relatively subordinate role in Thresholds, and at another time a board member, and thus essentially the boss. Perhaps when an agency is younger and less formed, and needs the manpower more, it can work out for board members to serve as volunteers. We've found that it creates problems for us."

Thresholds believes that it does not have legal responsibility for its members in the sense that a medical facility has. Said a member of the board, "While much that goes on here seems to be therapeutic, we believe after having explored the question that what we are doing is not 'treatment' within the usual legal meaning of the term. People come and go voluntarily. They get their medications elsewhere. We do have a professional consultant, but by and large we believe that we would not be legally responsible for any harm that came to a member."

The current casework organization of staff is into three teams. This facilitates participation, prevents any one person from monopolizing discussion, and enables staff to discuss cases in greater depth. One of the two staff meetings is used for "team meetings." Each team has a senior staff worker as leader; the executive director, assistant director, and director of social rehabilitation serve in this capacity. Each team is composed of a balance of personalities, attributes, professionality, experience, and as many other factors as the agency can muster in five people per team.

There is another program structure that cuts across this. The staff that covers the vocational area reports to the assistant director in this area. The staff that handles the social rehabilitation reports to the supervisor for that area.

Informality pervades the staff relationships at Thresholds. Rarely is any person, staff member or client, addressed as Mr. or Miss; rather, first names are used consistently. In most cases one would be hard put to differentiate clients from staff. There seems to be a minimum of privacy (and isolation) within the building. No staff member's office, including the director's, is impervious to interruptions or the constant ringing of telephones.

Physical facilities

Thresholds is located in a four-story brownstone house on the Near North Side of Chicago, convenient to public transportation; a subway stop is less than two blocks away. The area in which Thresholds is located is a rather anonymous, somewhat transitional neighborhood, within a few blocks of the commercial and entertainment sections of the central city.

The building, once a large private home, is old. While neither elaborate nor pretentious, it is reasonably attractive, at the same time conveying a well-used if not somewhat run-down feeling.

The first floor contains a large and comfortably furnished living room, a dining room, and a small kitchen. The living room is used for general social purposes. The dining room, in addition to furnishing room for lunches and coffee breaks, provides additional space for social activities.

The second floor contains offices for the professional staff and a large room that serves both as a workroom for the prevocational clerical program and as a center for social activities and group meetings during the social program hours. It is also used for dancing, Ping-pong, and similar activities.

The third floor contains administrative and clerical offices. The basement has a pool table, a large kitchen, and a crafts room. A patio in the rear has been fixed up for barbecues and similar outdoor activities.

All in all the house seems cramped, although it appeared that its shortcomings seem more pressing to the staff than to the members. In any case, privacy is hard to come by, and an uninterrupted private

interview seems nearly impossible. The crowding heightens and drama-
tizes the impression of activity and vitality that pervades the house.

The staff

The combined staff of the central Thresholds program plus its satellites
consists of twenty full-time and seven part-time staff members, plus 17
VISTA volunteers, eight summer volunteers, and fifty "regular" volunteers. However, we shall discuss the staff of the satellites separately and
will be concerned here only with the staff at the central facility.

There are nine professional staff, all trained at the bachelor's or master's level in the fields of psychology, social work, and rehabilitation.
They are backed up by five full-time and one part-time clerical staff
and seven VISTA volunteers. There is a four-fifths-time research associate, a one-fifth-time research consultant, and a one-fifth-time case consultant.

The full-time professional staff have such titles as director of group
work, director of vocational placements, and intake director, but these
titles for the most part represent only a particular, specialized part of
their function. Diffuseness of responsibility and blurring of roles have
been incorporated to a great extent in the staffing of Thresholds. For
the most part, each staff member has three basic elements to his job.
Everybody has a caseload, everybody runs a group, and everybody has
some major additional specialized responsibility. For example, one supervises volunteers, one runs the group job programs, and another the
individual job placement. Staff members meet one afternoon a week
for three hours, and attend the "team meeting" where they discuss current problems and evaluate the progress of each member.

Mr. Dincin feels that the core ingredient in each member's relationship with the agency lies in his "rehabilitative" relationship with a particular member of the staff. The members, being for the most part
chronically ill, must have some fully responsible staff person with whom
to relate in order to be able to make progress. Most staff members are
carrying ten to thirteen Thresholds members; the anticipated maximum
caseload is twenty, but at no time thus far has this been reached. When
that time comes, it will be necessary either to augment the staff, close
intake, or get a larger building, since the physical capacity of the building controls in some measure the number of members.

Thus, each staff member is expected to serve both as a generalist and
as a specialist, and in addition is expected to carry out social group
responsibilities. For his individual clients he is both coordinator and
follow-up worker. This varied combination of responsibilities seemed

to be perceived by the staff as an interesting and valued aspect of working at Thresholds. It also seemed to assure that no staff member would become isolated in routine, and that a high load of variety and challenge can as a result be built into each job.

Says a Thresholds report of this type of staff assignment:

> We think that there is a particular kind of relationship that needs to be engendered in a rehabilitation setting with members such as ours. The worker primarily must be an activist; that is, he must help to bridge the gap between intake and acceptable participation in the program. He must be active in creating a social role for the member while he attends the agency, of supporting it, and crystallizing for the member the positive results of this role. Thus, the worker must be professionally tenacious in the face of strong negative symptomatology —regression, hostility, and resistance. He must exhibit a strong professional desire to initiate change in his client. He must maintain a deep-seated broad interest in all areas of a member's current life.

Mr. Dincin was at Fountain House for five years, following which he directed Friendship House in Hackensack, New Jersey, and Prospect House in East Orange, New Jersey, two small psychosocial rehabilitation centers that were started as branches of Fountain House and later became independent centers. Thus, as of 1970 he had spent all twelve years of his career in psychiatric rehabilitation.

The assistant director, whose responsibilities include supervision of the vocational program, administrative duties, and program development, came to Thresholds after five years on the staff at Fountain House, where he had been in charge of liaison with the Division of Vocational Rehabilitation. He left Fountain House to seek an opening that had more administrative responsibility, and found such an opportunity at Thresholds.

Thresholds uses three psychiatric consultants for two hours per week each. These are respectively responsible for medication management, case review, and "agency milieu" discussion. A fourth consultant is a psychiatric caseworker who spends one day a week meeting with staff members to discuss case management. Judging from the reaction of staff members we interviewed, this person seemed to be playing a useful role, at least in part because he provided an outside perspective on some of the management problems that staff members found themselves embroiled in.

Volunteers

Approximately fifty active volunteers devote about three hours a week each to the Thresholds program, acting as hosts and hostesses, helping in the research program, and leading such groups as grooming, dramatics, and sewing, and in "social placements." Mr. Dincin expresses the view that "by and large, volunteers are worth the effort that we put out for them, even though it does take a good deal of time to train and supervise them."

Nonetheless, Thresholds depends less on volunteers now than it has at times in the past, for several reasons. One is the fact that the ratio of paid staff to members has improved. Another has been the availability since 1967 of a large corps of VISTA volunteers—17 as of the time of our visit. Some of these have presented problems, but the ones that we interviewed seemed particularly energetic and highly motivated. They work an average of 45 hours per week.

We were surprised to learn from Thresholds staff members that they do not feel they have been particularly successful in recruiting volunteers —because they do have a large number involved in the program, and because they have arranged with the YMCA Community College to offer a nine-week training course in serving as a volunteer at Thresholds. Two staff members, and sometimes more, are involved in teaching this course. Approximately sixty volunteers have participated in this course since it was established in 1968. Other volunteers are trained on the spot at Thresholds.

One interesting volunteer assignment unique to Thresholds is the practice of having the volunteer and a member assigned to him jointly become members of some community organization such as a church social, a "Y" group, or a political party. In this program component, supervised by a member of the staff, about 35 volunteers and 35 Thresholds members have joined community groups. There is a monthly group meeting of these volunteers, at which time each turns in a written report. Telephone contact and informal supervision characterize this aspect of the program. Other program volunteers meet weekly.

The limited Saturday program of social events is run entirely by volunteers.

The members

Thresholds describes its target population as persons who are between the ages of eighteen and fifty, who have a history of mental illness and a deficit therefrom that appears to require community-based rehabilitation services. The age limits were set because of the belief that before eighteen the schizophrenic youngster's problems may be exacerbated by his teen-age problems. After fifty, there are various psychological as well as physiological changes in the individual that may complicate the rehabilitative processes, and the vocational prognosis is usually poor. Even so the age limits are not rigidly observed, and in 1969 approximately four percent of the members were below eighteen and ten percent above fifty.

Thresholds accepts both men and women, and the sex distribution of new members accepted into the program during 1969 was about fifty-fifty; about 75 percent of those who become members have never been married. Similarly, there are no restrictions based on race, and in 1969 about fifteen percent of the members were black (compared to about forty percent of the state hospital population from the Chicago area).

At an earlier time, in response to Social and Rehabilitation Service research requirements, Thresholds accepted only prospective members who had been diagnosed as schizophrenic. More recently, this requirement has been dropped. "More and more we have found that the traditional diagnostic categories are irrelevant, and we have grown less and less used to using them," Mr. Dincin told us. Nonetheless, he estimates the Thresholds membership as about eighty percent schizophrenic, ten percent other psychotic diagnoses, and ten percent neurotic diagnoses. There is no requirement that a member have been a patient in a hospital, although about 95 percent of those who were active members during 1969 had been hospitalized one or more times.

Referrals and intake

Intake is initiated at Thresholds with an intake worker who was trained as a vocational counselor. She prefers in all possible cases for the applicant to make his own telephone call to obtain an appointment. In any case, at the time of the first call an appointment is made for him to come to Thresholds, often within a day or two and rarely more than a week. If an agency has made the call either for the client or as well as the client, Thresholds requests that some background information be sent.

Importance is attached to having the prospective member make his own telephone call in the hope that the conversation with the staff member will be a step, even if preliminary and tenuous, in helping the applicant "become attached to the agency, to feel that he has done something, however little, to try to help himself."

The initial meeting with the intake worker usually lasts about an hour. During this time the applicant fills out a set of forms and answers some background questions, designed to provide some descriptive data that may be useful in formulating a program. During this first visit the applicant is invited to attend a coffee session with members. This gives him "a chance to see others like himself being guided and aided in both social and vocational rehabilitation programs."

During the first visit the applicant is given literature on the Thresholds program and encouraged to return the following day for an orientation session which is the second step of the intake process. On that second day, the intake worker answers any questions the applicant may have. He joins another coffee session. In the event there are other prospective members, he has an opportunity to socialize with them as well. At this point he is taken on a tour of the building and introduced to the supervisor of each work area, of whom he can ask questions about each particular aspect of the program.

The applicant is invited to return the following day for a second orientation meeting led by the director. By now, hopefully, he feels more comfortable and will have more questions about how he might fit into the program. If he has problems about a place to live, money, medication, or anything else relative to his participating in the program, they are dealt with at this point. The entire orientation period is designed to help him develop a feeling of attachment and membership that will encourage him to want to continue to come and to use the program. "For the most part," says a Thresholds report, "the total environmental setting of Thresholds is much more happy and encouraging to the schizophrenic than was his setting in the hospital."

The next step is a review of the applicant by the Thresholds staff. At meetings held each week, each prospective member is "staffed" by the intake worker. The list of new applicants is discussed and passed on to one "team" who share responsibility for reaching out to new members for one further week. The person is considered a member at intake.

On the first day of his regular tenure he reports to his caseworker for a personal interview. "The staff worker encourages him to participate fully in the program, encourages total commitment to the agency's policies, and gives the member the positive reinforcement he needs to get started in the right direction."

As with all other such agencies, there is a high dropout rate. Only about eighty percent of those who telephone for an initial appointment show up. Of those who start the intake process, only about 75 percent complete it. Says a Thresholds report:

> ... it is our impression that most of the people who do not return were too frightened or had symptoms that were too overwhelming for them to participate. A few had already attained a satisfactory level of adjustment and would not benefit further from our program. The group closed at intake represents 25 percent of the total terminated

cases at Thresholds, and although it may not be an irreducible minimum, it is fairly close to it in view of our intake policy [which is to exercise] only minimal screening at intake; that is, we screen out only people who are grossly inappropriate. . . . Where there is the slightest hope that a person might make use of our services we include him in the intake group and work with him if possible toward participation in the program.

One dilemma confronting Thresholds—and other agencies working with a mentally ill population—is the inability to predict at intake whom they will be able to help. "We are consistently surprised and out-guessed," says a Thresholds report.

A follow-up is made on any member who has not shown up during the previous week. An effort is first made to reach him by telephone. In rare cases, when there is no telephone, a home visit is made. Those who have "dropped out" after a period of time in the program are frequently those who have regressed because they have stopped taking their medication. Only occasionally is a "dropout" the result of a person's having dramatically improved to the point that he has been able to go out on his own initiative and find a job.

The program, in general

Once a new member has completed the intake and orientation process, he is eligible for service from Thresholds for a period up to one year. Actually, exceptions to the time limit are frequently made, since a number of those who stick with the program seem to be on the brink of some accomplishment at about the expiration of the year, and consequently at any given time a moderate percentage of the active membership will have been participating for a few months longer. In a very few instances members have been kept active for as long as two years, "because they always seemed to be about to accomplish something or have just done so and need support."

During the early years, there was no time limit on participation in the Thresholds program. Mr. Dincin told us:

> When I came in 1965, the agency was filled to capacity and intake was closed. Our clients were the most chronic and had the poorest prognoses, and we had in fact become the final resting place for Chicago's chronic ambulatory schizophrenic population. The board of directors, in a long series of meetings, worked out a plan to hire a consultant. At his urging and mine they changed the concept to one of a time-limited service, in order to become a rehabilitation center. Accordingly, we gave the current members a further year, but set a one-year limit for new members. We feel that we can accomplish

pretty much what we have to offer within a year. We have set certain standards and criteria by which we evaluate what we accomplish, but we have not at all gone into a study of optimal length of participation for various categories of clients; this is decided individually, primarily through relationships of the members to their caseworkers. This has by now ceased to be a problem either among the staff or among the members. They simply accept this as the ethic of the agency and go along with it.

The member who has completed the intake may be in one of three statuses. He may be a "regular" member, who spends the morning assigned to one of several vocational crews that meet and work at the house, and his afternoons in various social rehabilitation groups which, for the most part, he is free to select. Or he may be a "working" member; i.e., he may spend his mornings in a group placement and his afternoons in the social program at the agency. Or he may have graduated to regular employment and then come to Thresholds only for the Tuesday and Thursday evening and/or the Saturday social programs.

Thus, each member has vocational training, socialization experiences, and supportive individual counseling available to him. Since each client is assigned to the caseload of a particular staff member, from these assignments partly supportive, partly therapeutic, partly follow-up relationships develop. It becomes the staff worker's responsibility to know the locus and status of each of his clients at all times, to be aware of progress, to monitor participation, and to reach out, as necessary, to retrieve the client if he shows signs of wavering or disaffiliating himself from the program.

Certain activities are described as "mandatory," specifically the rehabilitation groups which meet on Monday afternoons, and, for those who are working, an evening rehabilitation group and a placement group. But in actuality they are not mandatory, since those who fail to attend are not discharged from the program. It would be more accurate to say that the member is strongly advised that the groups are mandatory and that it is hoped that he will respond accordingly. Those who attend the day program are given carfare and lunch money, and this can of course be withheld. But such sanctions are on the face of it self-defeating.

Rules are presented to members orally and do not exist in written form. They are few in number. The most important is that members must never use physical force toward fellow members. Infractions can result in suspension or expulsion, but this has rarely been necessary.

People who have dropped out of the program or who have left by mutual consent and later have relapsed are sometimes readmitted to the program. "If they left prior to the full year, for any reason at all, we usually welcome them back," Mr. Dincin said. A study of reopened cases disclosed that members in Thresholds do not do better "the second time around."

The social program

The relative emphasis between vocational and social activities at Thresholds has changed from time to time. Said Mr. Dincin:

> Thresholds started strictly as a social club, and then in 1963 the vocational program was added, and for several years was heavily emphasized. Then, around 1967 we began to feel, on the basis of some of the research we did, that we seemed to be doing well in the vocational area but that our members, when they stopped coming to Thresholds, were doing very poorly in the social area. They were not doing anything out in the community to integrate themselves in a normal social way. And thus we have moved the balance recently somewhat further in the direction of social rehabilitation. At this moment I would estimate that about sixty percent of our effort is in the vocational area, the other forty in the social area.

While Thresholds offers during the course of each week more than thirty scheduled social activities of numerous kinds, it appears to consider the very fact of its availability as a clubhouse to be "the core of the group services program." This availability of its facilities on a come-as-you-will basis it refers to as "the lounge program." This means simply that whenever Thresholds is open any member may come to the clubhouse, where there are opportunities for conversation, piano playing, reading, cards, Scrabble, pool, Ping-pong, and record playing. Also part of this clubhouse program are the cooking activities in the kitchen, used to prepare refreshments for scheduled events. Throughout the afternoon and evening there is coffee available in the dining room. Supper is prepared by the members before the Tuesday and Thursday evening programs and on Sunday.

This availability is currently being de-emphasized in favor of a social group work approach with a fairly high expectation level.

It is important to realize that the lounge program, unstructured and undemanding though it may be, is not by any means seen as the entry point or the lowest level of participation. The thirty or so weekly programmed activities may for a given member represent either a higher or a lower level of participation than the lounge program. In any case, the programmed activities provide a structure that the lounge program does not have. "The particular activity which is provided serves as a focus of attention, and the individual can relate to the activity itself rather than to other individuals, if this is his need." These groups provide a focus for conversation, roles to play, and motions to go through. The individual can be sheltered, if that is his need, by the presence and involvement of the leader, who sets limits, states goals, and, when necessary, directs action.

In the course of a week there are approximately twenty daytime "interest" and "activity" groups, including grooming, sewing, the Thresholds newspaper, a charm class, a copper and enameling class, a fancy baking class, weight lifting, card games, improvisations, "exploring the arts," and a dating group and three "mandatory" rehabilitation groups. On Tuesday and Thursday evenings there are ten groups, including a dramatics group, a card group, a photography club. The principal difference in the interest groups, the social clubs, and the activity groups is that any member may choose to attend any of the interest groups he wishes, whereas entry into the social clubs and activity groups is on recommendation by the staff member, in terms of the particular goals he has in mind for his client. The referred member must then be accepted by the group leader as able to use the group appropriately.

Among the scheduled activities are some, such as psychodrama, that smack of therapy, and others, such as "the world of work," that have as much of the prevocational as of the recreational/social.

On Saturday afternoons the volunteer-led "extension courses" take place. This program is led by VISTA workers and staffed by college students. They have eight-week courses in typing, high-school diploma equivalency, public speaking, crafts, and other subjects that the strengths and interests of the volunteers provide and that suit the needs of the members. There is a small charge for this program. From fifteen to thirty members attend.

Sunday is an informal lounge program, featuring a movie and supper. Attendance averages about twenty.

Vocational program

Thresholds considers that getting its members into employment is an integral component of the rehabilitation plan "and not some kind of separate service." Placements are of several types, but all are part time, ranging up to twenty hours per week. All employers know that each person placed is a member of Thresholds and has a history of mental illness.

Thresholds members who are not ready for a work placement under any of the four provisions described below are occupied each morning in a prevocational work adjustment program at the Thresholds facility. These assignments have mainly to do with the operation of the facility, and are grouped in six program areas: clerical, painting, housekeeping, food services, sewing, and maintenance. These are all supervised by staff members who work along with the members.

Of the four types of placements, the least demanding is the "Thresholds-paid placement." Under this arrangement a member goes to some place of business, or more often a social agency such as a Jewish community center and the Sisters of Jude, where he performs "volunteer" work, for which he is paid $1 per hour by Thresholds. The "employer" pays nothing. The hours are arranged to meet the member's work tolerance and can range from as little as two to as many as twenty hours per week. The member is expected to be able to produce even if at a limited level, to be appropriate in appearance, and to "have a workmanlike attitude." Thresholds sees this arrangement as a good one both for particular members and for the employers.

> It serves to reduce the expectation that the employer has for the member. This is important, since it reduces the member's anxiety on the job. The employer feels he is getting some help and not paying for it and tends to be flexible in his handling of the member, amenable to suggestions, and generally in better communication with the agency. . . . It has been our experience that when the member has worked for a period, the employer feels uncomfortable about the lack of remuneration and begins to pay something for the work done.

For those whose productivity and work habits and skills are a bit better, there is the "employer-Thresholds shared-pay plan," with the employer paying part and the agency paying the rest of an hourly wage. As the worker increases in productivity and proves his ability, the employer pays an increasing share of the salary. These jobs range in time from four to twenty hours per week.

Thresholds reports that for both of the above kinds of placement the vocational counselors must exercise extreme care to see that the employer does not exploit the member, as has occasionally happened "with a very passive member, an aggressive employer, and a physically distant job location."

At a still higher level are part-time jobs for which the employer pays the going wage. In these placements there is little distinction between the Thresholds employee and regular employees. These jobs usually range from ten to 35 hours per week. The larger firms tend to require a full workweek "since they do not have the flexibility to allow for the wage plans mentioned in the first two situations."

The final type of job is the group placement, patterned on that of Fountain House and initiated by Thresholds late in 1969. The only such placement at the time of our visit was in a downtown cafeteria, where seven Thresholds members were working as busboys and dishwashers, under the eye of a VISTA volunteer from the Thresholds staff. These men worked from four to twenty hours per week and were being paid at the rate of $1.60 per hour. The placement was located through the help of a board member.

Thresholds has a vocational placement director who seeks out jobs and maintains contacts with employers.

Members who are on any of the four types of job placement must maintain close and regular contact with Thresholds. Those who are consistently remiss in this respect can be taken off the placement, although this has happened only occasionally. This requirement is carefully explained to members when they are being offered a placement, and it seems to be quite well observed for a period of time. "This is one reason why there is a limitation of twenty hours per week on most job placements," we were told. "The remainder of the time the member is expected to attend the Thresholds program to work on some aspect of his rehabilitation and to solidify his gains. . . . Bitter experience has taught us that members tend to fail when the support of the agency is withdrawn or when they withdraw from the agency. Essential contact is also maintained at the job placement meeting, held weekly on Tuesday evenings. All members on placement are required to attend this meeting, to discuss such topics as job relationships, work attitudes, promptness, initiative, attitudes towards supervision, and grossly inappropriate behavior."

Thresholds reports that in general its more successful placements have been with small firms or in jobs at larger firms where the member is exposed to only a few co-workers.

> The most successful transitional employment situations exist where the employer is both the owner of the business and an active participant in the supervision of the client. Of key importance in the success of all placements, irrespective of size, is seemingly the fact that one person has primary supervisory responsibility for the client and is with him throughout the bulk of his work time. This makes for a consistency and stability of relationship with work assignments, work demands, and work expectations being clearly defined and minimizing a repetition of contradictory and double-bind experiences for the client.

At the time of our visit Thresholds was in process of creating an "employers council" consisting of representatives of the approximately twelve firms that provide the agency's approximately twenty placements.

A sheltered workshop. Thresholds has created on the North Side of Chicago, in a dreary and downward-moving neighborhood, a very exciting sheltered workshop. Housed in a somewhat ramshackle loft, it impressed the authors as one of the best such programs any of them had seen. Staffed by a director, two staff assistants, and eight VISTA volunteers, the program serves about fifty active clients who spend an average of about four hours each working day at a variety of simple contract jobs, such as sorting and assembling. In addition to the hours spent at work, each member spends some time with a counselor and participates in one or more of a few social activities that are offered. The work is organized so that a certain limited amount of social interaction is necessary, and one afternoon a week the participants break up into seven- and eight-person groups for discussion about the goals of work. Thus, as with the parent facility, there is an effort to integrate vocational and social goals.

Good lunches are prepared by the members and sold for ten cents. The members plan the meals, shop for the food, prepare it, serve it, and clean up afterward.

A few of these members are referred to the workshop from the parent Thresholds facility, but the majority come from the "psychiatric hotels" in which the Illinois state hospitals place discharged patients.

The director seemed apologetic for the appearance of the workshop and spoke of the limited capabilities of the members. But compared with other workshops, the North Side branch conveyed no atmosphere of regression or stagnation, and for so chronic a group of members it seemed to be a remarkable success.

As we were leaving we saw a fairly young man sitting at the bottom of the stairs sulking. The staff had refused to allow him to come for lunch because he had refused to work in the morning program. This seemed an example of the kind of structured limit that is appropriately put on undermotivated people, as well as a good way to keep the shop from deteriorating into a group of people who are staring into space.

Residential program

Thresholds makes no particular requirement about where its members live. Some live at home, some alone, others at the various "psychiatric hotels." Often Thresholds helps an incoming member to find a place to live.

It does not, however, operate "live in" facilities, except in a limited and specialized sense. Specifically, it has leased the building next door, which was formerly a rooming house. As the original tenants have moved out, Thresholds members have been moved in. By early 1970 the mixture among the residents was fifty percent Thresholds members and fifty percent regular tenants. The Thresholds members pay the regular rental fee of $75 per month. One staff member lives there, but no therapeutic intervention is offered except in an emergency. There have been no particular problems in intermixing the Thresholds members and other residents, or pertaining to the behavior of Thresholds members.

Thresholds has recently concluded an agreement with a small hotel containing sixty residents, to whom Thresholds provides professional rehabilitation services. As rooms become available, Thresholds members have a good chance of getting them. This has proved advantageous for all concerned, even though quite a bit of Thresholds' staff time is involved.

Medication

"We have become increasingly sophisticated in our understanding that medication for psychiatric patients is another key factor in their continued recovery," says a Thresholds report. "We do not usually prescribe at the agency, but we are aware of the medicine our members are taking, and the side effects, and very often are able to recommend that an evaluation of the medication be undertaken by psychiatric consultants."

At the same time, Thresholds does not require that each of its members have a particular psychiatrist or other therapeutic backup. "Because of the nature of mental health resources and how they are organized in Chicago," we were told, "this would be an unrealistic requirement. More than half of our members are on welfare, and very little is available in the way of therapeutic backup. Some of the 'psychiatric hotels' have someone to check medication." Even so, Thresholds does have a psychiatric consultant who comes each week for two hours to take care of anyone who has not been able to get medication service elsewhere.

Families

For a good many years Thresholds deliberately did not attempt to have any dealings with the families of its members, on the theory that it was probably best "to leave families out of the therapeutic milieu, since very often they prove to be quite unhelpful." More recently it has started the practice of inviting parents or other relatives to a two-session evening orientation meeting, repeated monthly. "We have not been exactly overjoyed with the healthy level of parental participation," Mr. Dincin told us. In any case, from the orientation group Thresholds tries to identify families who would be more interested in or accessible to group therapy. Several such groups have been held, with moderately good progress in terms of effecting a healthy change in the relationship of the member to his family. "We will keep this up," Mr. Dincin said, "for the sake of that small percentage who can benefit from it; but most relatives are unable or unwilling to use this service."

Agency and community relationships

Thresholds is located in an anonymous "intown" section of Chicago, surrounded by businesses, restaurants, rooming houses, and apartment buildings. In appearance it seems very much like its neighboring buildings. There have been no problems at all with any of the merchants or neighbors. Its members come and go freely without interference. Mr. Dincin characterized Thresholds as having been "relatively isolated from the community."

Within the mental health community, Thresholds has been given the assignment of helping to plan for comprehensive mental health services in the "near north area" of Chicago. Mr. Dincin is chairman of "long range mental health planning" for the community in which Thresholds is located.

We have mentioned the limited involvement in the program of the "psychiatric hotels." At two of these hotels Thresholds helped to set up terminal workshops. It has not been involved in staffing these facilities but has helped to obtain contracts, pick up and deliver materials and products, and provide consultation, in a "facilitative role."

Among the few contractual arrangements are important ones with the Illinois Division of Vocational Rehabilitation and the State Department of Mental Health, described below.

Training

In the past, Thresholds allowed the rotation of some psychiatric residents through the agency but their role was ill defined and they tended to relate in a traditional psychotherapeutic role. Some fitted in well, most did not, and this type of training was phased out.

Currently, Thresholds trains second-year group workers from the University of Chicago School of Social Service Administration, and a first- and a second-year community organization student from the same school. These students spend three days a week for a full year and receive close supervision. The agency also trains rehabilitation students from DePaul University and Illinois Institute of Technology.

The training efforts are limited only by Mr. Dincin's unwillingness to remove supervisors from direct program responsibility and to free them for students, since a number of schools have expressed an interest in placing students at Thresholds.

Financing

Thresholds operates with a total budget of approximately $375,000, but this figure includes $136,000 in a special grant from the National Institute of Mental Health to run a demonstration program for adolescents which is quite different in nature from the psychosocial rehabilitation program. Thus, the portion of the budget that involves the activities within the scope of this study is about $238,000. The largest portion of this—thirty percent—comes from the State Department of Mental Health, in the form of a block grant, the justification for which is that Thresholds is essentially the only Chicago-based facility whose target population is by and large the persons who have formerly been in state mental hospitals. The next largest amount, about 28 percent, comes from the State Division of Vocational Rehabilitation, in the form of compensation for Personal Adjustment Training services purchased from Thresholds. Next come individual contributions—about $46,000 or 19 percent. These funds are solicited by the board members from their friends. The director and a small committee handle the solicitation of local corporations and foundations through letters and personal calls. Foundations and organizations provide about $23,000 or ten percent. Five percent comes from several smaller sources, one of which is members' dues, which in 1969 came to only $2000.

Thresholds began to charge fees about 1967, "as part of a program to break members' overdependency upon Thresholds and to help change the 'all-giving mother image' that we had developed." Mr. Dincin reported that at first there was considerable staff resistance to charging fees or dues, even though the amount was nominal, and he related this to "the insecurity of the staff about the value of their services," but added that this problem seems to have been substantially overcome. In any case, all members, even those living on welfare payments, are charged something, from $1 a week upward. Daytime members pay on the average $5 per month, and evening members from $7 to $8 per month. For those relatively few parents who attend the therapy group, there is a fee of $5 per week per couple.

Outcome

Thresholds has made some fairly simple attempts to ascertain the effectiveness of its program. In 1968 the staff analyzed various demographic characteristics of members in relation to outcome. They also made an analysis in respect of length of stay, and a study of condition of members at time of terminating from the program.

The 1963-68 study, done under a Social and Rehabilitation Service grant, compared persons provided with the complete Thresholds program with those provided only the socialization (that is, not the vocational) services, and those who underwent no rehabilitation program at all. Those offered the complete program achieved a better work adjustment than the other two groups; specifically, 22 percent of them were in continuous, competitive employment at the end of a two-year period, while none of the members offered only the social program were so employed. Fifty-six percent of those offered the whole program were not in any employment status at all at the end of the period, compared with 68 percent of the other groups.

The status of members terminated in 1967 and 1968 was determined by means of a rating scale developed for use within Thresholds. The 125 persons who completed the intake process and were then terminated during 1968 fell into the following categories: *a*) made no firm connection with the program, 15 persons or 12 percent; *b*) were considered to be substantially improved, 48 persons or 38 percent; *c*) were unchanged, 46 persons or 37 percent; *d*) were in worse condition at time of termination than when they entered the program, 14 persons or 11 percent; *e*) miscellaneous, two persons or two percent.

Mr. Dincin and the staff use four areas of activity to judge the effectiveness of the program. These are *a*) community social life, *b*) vocational adjustment, *c*) independent living, and *d*) control of symptomatology. For each of these areas an uncomplicated rating scale of about fifteen items has been developed. These are completed by the staff at intake, at three-month intervals, at termination, and six months after termination. In this way, they hope to chart changes in the member which have potential effectiveness.

It is clear that Mr. Dincin and his staff want very much to know whether their services are useful and helpful, and they have plans to make more extensive and sophisticated research studies in the near future.

Plans for the future

Thresholds has identified several areas in which changes, expansion, or improvements seem to be needed, specifically:

1. A new physical plant is seen as essential. "We are outgrowing our present one and our program will be stifled if we remain here."

2. A branch should be established on the South Side of Chicago in the interest of serving larger numbers of Negroes. In 1968, only fifteen percent of the terminated cases were black, whereas the proportion in the state hospital from the Chicago area is forty percent.

3. The service should be broadened to include additional kinds of clients. "Our unique capabilities in rehabilitation, our connections within the community, our nonclinical background all place us in an advantageous position to do this."

4. Residential capacity both for adolescents and adults should be substantially increased.

5. There should be an enhanced focus on outcome data and research material.

There has also been some interest in and discussion of the possibility that Thresholds might become part and parcel of a community mental health center, in conjunction with the Northwestern University Department of Psychiatry. If it should be possible for this to come about, the center would serve a varied population of about 200,000, which Mr. Dincin feels would need to be served through decentralized neighborhood "storefront" facilities.

X. Portals House
Los Angeles

PORTALS IS A COMMUNITY REHABILITATION AGENCY that has undergone substantial change in the past three years and evidently will continue to do so for some time to come. Having started as a small halfway house, it had by late 1969 become redirected into a program emphasizing social rehabilitation and providing residence through contractual arrangement with proprietary board-and-care homes. Its application for financially participating membership in the United Fund was approved to begin in 1970, and a Social and Rehabilitation Service Facility Improvement Grant is pending.

Origins

Portals in its original form was the brainchild of Mrs. Shirley Weiss and Mrs. Sybil Brand who, in 1953, while working as volunteers at Brentwood Veterans Administration Hospital, were increasingly disturbed that many discharged patients soon returned. The halfway house was something of a pioneering notion at that early time, still a year or two before the introduction of psychotropic drugs.

They obtained from the administration of the hospital an assurance that if a transitional residence were started in the community the hospital would send referrals. With a $5000 grant from the Hollywood Canteen, the program was started for ten men in mid-1955, in a small rented house. "There was no publicity, deliberately," Mrs. Weiss told us. "At that time most people were afraid to have anything to do with such an effort; we went to the Welfare Planning Council and to the Community Chest, and they told us we were ten years ahead of the times. They told us the community was not ready to have mental patients running around in the neighborhood, so they advised us not to tell the neighbors."

There was scarcely any income because the initial concept was that, save for a housekeeper and caretaker who slept in, paid staff was not necessary. Professionals at Brentwood Veterans Administration Hospital committed themselves to provide volunteer professional services.

This lasted less than a year and it was necessary to employ a part-time social worker as director. Two years later this position was increased to full time. The initial thinking was that this was an inexpensive program to operate. Therefore the initial board was not committed to "serious" fund raising or personal financial commitment. The program developed at a satisfactory pace, and in 1959 the nonprofit corporation that administered the program purchased the house. In 1962 a second house was developed for eleven women, and it too was purchased. The agency continued in this vein for some time, as one of the pioneering programs in transitional residence but with relatively little other program.

In 1963 the board undertook a major re-examination of the agency's purposes, programs, and effectiveness. As a means of appraising the program, an independent study followed up the 51 men and 49 women who had "graduated" from the halfway house. In 1965 a new executive director, Marvin Weinstein, a social worker, was hired. He was sent to Fountain House in New York, Horizon House in Philadelphia, and Thresholds in Chicago to inquire into these more comprehensive programs.

Based on the feelings of the new director, and concerned by the somewhat problematic findings of the follow-up study, the board of trustees radically changed its philosophy and program in late 1966. At that time it sold the men's residence and a year later the women's residence, and undertook a new nonresidential approach emphasizing social and to a lesser extent vocational rehabilitation services on a community basis. Consequently, we are concerned here only with approximately the past three years.

Philosophy, purpose, and policy

The target population for Portals is the young adult, from 18 to 35, with an average age of 22. Most have been hospitalized, primarily in state hospitals, for mental disorder, but no particular attention is paid to diagnosis as such. Exclusions are based instead on behavior—specifically, the severely assaultive, the habitual user of hard narcotics, and the alcoholic. The avoidance of alcoholics is particularly strong among all the staff, not so much because of their getting drunk but because in past experiences alcoholics have been destructive to the house and its furnishings, manipulative, and overly demanding of staff time. Alcoholics, narcotics users, and the assaultive "require a close and highly structured setting, which we do not provide, because of our philosophy of requiring a high degree of personal responsibility," we were told.

Any person with problems in social functioning other than those described above is welcome to apply, provided the referral comes through a social worker or a physician. Self-referrals are simply not accepted, on the basis that sending for and compiling their records is too time-consuming for the small Portals staff. (This is to be changed with the addition of a social worker assigned full time to intake duties.)

The program emphasizes service to young adults because it believes they have in common certain adjustment problems such as peer relationships, family separation, sexual relationships, and vocational needs. While these are problems shared by all age groups, Portals feels that intervention has greater possibilities with the younger age group; and through specialization it hopes eventually to become expert in working with the young adult.

More recently there has been a limited shift of emphasis from the state hospital population to any younger adults who have emotional problems affecting their functioning.

We observed in the course of our visit that severity of pathology certainly did not seem to be a deterrent to Portals. We attended a specially called meeting of the patients "to rap with the people from Washington, who are going to write a book about us," at which some highly disturbed behavior was in evidence. We concluded that while Portals may feel threatened by certain behaviors that it associates with the alcoholic, for example, certainly it is not threatened by the person with a psychosis that is not very well in remission. That the boarding home operators who provide residence for the Portals members have experienced no particular problem with some of these very disorganized members supports the view that one can be seriously impaired in certain functions and at the same time manage at least moderately well in many aspects of everyday living.

A social worker expressed an attitude toward community care of the mentally ill which seemed to reflect that of most of the Portals staff. She believes, as evidently the California Department of Mental Hygiene does, that mental institutions are passé and that patients must be provided with protection in the community rather than in institutions. She appears to see two kinds of patients who need this protection: those who are content to live on a welfare allowance in one of the board-and-care homes that have been set up by the Community Services Division of the Department of Social Welfare, with medication supervision and some degree of program entirely within the house; and those who want to get out from under the "totally disabled" label and thus to reintegrate themselves into society. Those who aspire to the latter course but cannot match up to it can be sent to the more protected situation.

In any case, the Portals staff appear to believe that everybody has a hidden capacity for improvement; although some will top off at less than "normal," as in a sheltered workshop, many others who seem to have topped off in reality have not. Portals thus appears to take a position that is a compromise between the obvious fact of disablement and the equally obvious fact that, even despite deficits, everyone can make some progress, even if very limited, toward a better level of functioning. Implicit in this is the belief that the more an individual is involved in making decisions about his own life, the more he will improve. Thus the belief in a multiplicity of socialization activities that strongly emphasize member responsibility.

The Portals viewpoint regarding public agencies was put forth by Mr. John Cohan, president of the board, who appears to believe that private agencies can work more effectively and at less cost to the taxpayer than public ones, and that therefore the public agencies should contract with private agencies so that they may do the job. Most of the Portals staff appeared to share his view that private agencies have more opportunity to be flexible and responsive to changing needs.

Management and administration

Portals is a nonprofit tax-exempt corporation governed by a board whose members serve for a maximum of six years. The number at the time of our visit was 23. The charter and bylaws call for trustees to be elected by a constituent membership, made up of about 600 mainly middle-income individuals who have made contributions ranging from $10 to $1000. The trustees are largely business and professional people.

The trustees are responsible for determining over-all agency policy. They employ an executive director who carries out the program authorized by the board, administers the program, and recruits and supervises staff. It appeared that the trustees and the staff were quite clear about their complementary roles.

There are no local or state licensure requirements for a service facility such as Portals, provided service is limited to those who are at least 16 and not more than 64 years old. The city and county require a permit for fund raising. The boardinghouses which have contracted to accept Portals members are required to conform to municipal regulations related principally to fire and health standards and not to program services.

Physical facilities

Portals is housed in a large, attractive, two-story building that was formerly a private home, in a quiet, residential neighborhood in the Wilshire section of Los Angeles, a few blocks from the commercial section. The first floor, with three large rooms plus a kitchen, is given over principally to the members. The upper floor is used as offices. In the rear is a pleasant patio area with a Ping-pong table and a shuffleboard court. A small rear building, a converted garage, houses the Portals House Canteen.

The staff

The small Portals staff consists of the executive director; two "case managers," one with a master's degree in rehabilitation counseling, the other with a master's degree in social work; two VISTA volunteers; a volunteer coordinator; an intake secretary; and two clerical workers. There are three "work-study students" assigned to Portals on a part-time basis.

As a group, the staff can be characterized as young, bright, relatively inexperienced, socially concerned, dedicated to the program and willing to assume unconventional roles within it, concerned with the quality of present services, and imbued with a feeling of building for the future. We were impressed with the positive feeling toward innovation and experimentation, as with the VISTA workers, who almost weekly improvise some new group or program.

Shortly before our visit there had been two resignations, those of the volunteer coordinator and a vocational counselor. As with almost all small agencies, this had led to a redefinition of roles, and while the responsibilities of particular staff members seemed fairly well worked out it was also evident that they had only recently become so and would probably be reworked again, perhaps several times, as experience and need indicate.

The executive director is required to have at least a master's degree, plus ten years of experience, five of which must be administrative or supervisory. His responsibilities include proposing programs and plans to the board, directing fund raising, preparing the annual budget, supervising collection, disbursement, and accounting for funds, and supervising the second-echelon staff members.

Mr. Weinstein, who has an extensive background in social group work, had worked in the Los Angeles area for about ten years, most of that time as director of Jewish Big Brothers, and subsequently as administrator of an antipoverty demonstration project. He learned of the Portals program when he was approached by a search committee seeking a replacement for a retiring executive director.

The rehabilitation counselor is responsible for "evaluation, case management, and movement of fifty clients through the Portals program and adjustment after they leave Portals." (She was handling forty clients at the time of our visit, since she shared the caseload with the group worker, and there were eighty active cases.) This position requires at least a master's degree in rehabilitation counseling, social work, or psychology, plus two years of experience. This staff member leads counseling groups —four at the time of our visit—and provides individual counseling services. The incumbent had been with Portals for almost two years, having come there directly from training. Her two-year graduate curriculum consisted "mainly of psychology with some emphasis on sociology and vocational counseling, but of a general nature with very little content about mental illness." Apart from a course in abnormal psychology, her training did not include any specific material about, for example, the typical living and behavior problems of the various categories of the mentally ill.

The social worker shares the caseload with the rehabilitation counselor. He too came to the program directly from training, following placement in psychiatric settings. He had casework experience prior to his professional training.

While these two staff members spend more than half of their time counseling individual members, almost all of this is on an informal, "as needed" basis. Typical problems concern conflicts with the landladies of the boardinghouses where most Portals members live, difficulties with roommates, relationships with relatives, medication, and so on.

The four groups which each of these staff members runs each week are the only components of the program compulsory for all members. Focusing on work, getting along with other people, etc., they are essentially problem-solving in orientation and are based on the approach of Dr. William Glasser. There are typically ten members in a group.

The two VISTA volunteers seem to constitute a sort of intermediate-level staff, beneath the case managers and above the work-study students. One had a bachelor's degree in psychology and had worked with crippled children, the other had a master's degree in personnel and guidance and had worked for some years as dean of women at a small college. They seemed talented but had no prior experience in working with the mentally ill. Both described themselves as "wanderers" who had been attracted to the stated purposes of VISTA. They underwent a three-week training course at the University of Oregon, followed by three weeks of inservice training at Portals, after which they were considered full-fledged VISTAs. They had performed in a variety of roles during the several months they had been at the agency, and at the time of our visit were in charge of the activities program; in this sense, they have a major element of control, in that they are responsible at any given moment for what activity a particular member present at the house is engaged in.

The work-study students are undergraduates whose education is subsidized 75 percent by grants originating in the Office of Economic Opportunity and 25 percent by the particular agency in which each is placed. They work a maximum of fifteen hours per week during school and forty hours during the summer. The placement and the student's curriculum are not necessarily related—in fact, in most cases are not. At Portals two work-study students are assigned as activity aides, the other as a clerk.

There are daily meetings of the staff, the last item of business for the day. These meetings are concerned mostly with current operating problems.

Portals is one of the first rehabilitation services dealing with the mentally ill to have requested accreditation from the Commission on Accreditation of Rehabilitation Facilities. "We requested accreditation," said Mr. Weinstein, "because as a nonmedical agency Portals needs external validation. Further, the accrediting process served as an excellent consultative resource and provided us an opportunity to consider future goals." Portals was approved for accreditation, with various suggestions for improvement. Those suggestions having to do specifically with staff were: *a*) that inservice training be substantially enhanced, with participation from a consulting psychologist; *b*) that there be a reference library for staff use; and *c*) that funds should be available to allow professional staff to attend pertinent conferences.

Volunteers

Portals has used volunteers extensively. During a recent year 36 volunteers contributed about 2900 hours, equivalent to about one and a half full-time staff members. The volunteers are used in several areas, particularly to help in the activities. They lead special interest groups, help prepare the Sunday buffet, orient new members, and lend a hand in the occasional larger outside activities such as beach parties. They are involved in a vocationally oriented evening group, a "multi-interest" evening group that consists of music, current events, and drama, a "satellite" evening group that schedules dances, movies, folk singing, and so on. Some are used as "community agents," assigned to members on an individual basis, much like Big Brothers or Big Sisters. They help the members with specific tasks, such as handling money and using public transportation.

There seems to have been no problem in recruiting volunteers. The agency had a list of more than a hundred applicants who would evidently be available for service if there were sufficient staff to supervise them. Ordinarily volunteers are anticipated to make a commitment of at least six months, and they must agree to accept supervision from the staff.

At the time of our visit the position of volunteer director was vacant, and it had been largely taken over by one of the volunteers, who had been involved in Portals for a little more than a year. At the time she came into the program volunteer activity was at an ebb, and she appeared herself to have had a large part in helping it to build up to approximately forty participants as of late 1969. About three quarters of the volunteers are women.

Volunteers attend the weekly "council meeting" of the members and from time to time participate in staff meetings. There were plans to establish a weekly evening "exit group" for members preparing to terminate their affiliation with Portals.

The two volunteers that we interviewed seemed to be enthusiastic and well informed about the objectives of Portals and highly committed to its continued growth. A volunteer committee in collaboration with the staff is responsible for orienting and assigning new volunteers.

Volunteers are not viewed—least of all by themselves—as merely additional man-hours to stopgap staff shortages. Said one that we interviewed:

> Our philosophy is to integrate people who have severe emotional stresses back into the community, and we feel that volunteers who are of the community have a vital role to play, because in one way or another we have learned how to adapt to and cope with the system.

The clientele

Eligibility. We have described above the exclusions that Portals has set. Beyond eliminating these particular groups, Portals appears to accept the considerable majority of referred persons who have a history of mental illness and appear to need and/or show promise of benefiting from a social rehabilitation program—*provided* they are able to produce from one source or another the $187.50 per month fee which covers the charges of the boardinghouses and the fee for Portals services. The considerable majority who are accepted by the program are financed under provisions of the welfare department's Aid to the Disabled program.

Age and sex. Portals occasionally departs from its 35-year-old upper age limit but never from its 18-year-old lower limit. For clients who entered the program during 1969, about three fifths were men. Nineteen percent of the men and 23 percent of the women were between 18 and 21. Seventy-two percent of the men and 69 percent of the women were between 21 and 40. Nine percent of the men and eight percent of the women were over 40.

Race. Most Portals members are native American Caucasians. Only about ten percent are Negroes and five percent of Mexican or other Latin-American origin. Mr. Weinstein attributed the low minority group membership to "stereotyping by referring agencies; we are in a white neighborhood. Most blacks are sent back to the ghetto. We plan to seek minority group members more aggressively in the future."

Residential status. Almost none of the members live with their parents—less than one percent. Well over ninety percent live in one of the boardinghouses which contract their services exclusively to Portals. A few members—perhaps ten out of an active caseload of eighty—have moved on to private apartments, either living alone or with fellow Portals members. A staff member estimated that if it were not for the particular funding pattern that encourages (almost makes mandatory) residence in one of the boardinghouses, probably half of the Portals membership would be capable of living in their own apartments.

Employment status. A higher percentage of Portals members than those of the other centers visited were working. The substantial majority are not working, of course, when they first come into the program, but many of them soon find either competitive or sheltered employment. Of the just under 300 persons who participated in the program at some time during 1969, 32 percent of the men and 45 percent of the women were working either full time or part time in competitive employment, and another 36 percent of the men and 31 percent of the women were working either full time or part time in some sheltered job, as at the Goodwill Industries. Thirty-one percent of the men and 24 percent of the women were not working at all. One of the boardinghouse operators whom we interviewed told us that of about 45 Portals members who live with her at a given time, from ten to twelve would be working in regular jobs.

Diagnosis. As with most of the other centers, Portals indicates that it pays no particular attention to and gets no particularly useful information from the diagnosis of the prospective member. Perhaps mainly because it works with a younger clientele, there are more character disorders here than in the other agencies (eleven percent of those who entered the program in 1969), but even so schizophrenia is the modal diagnosis, accounting for eighty percent. The rest are equally divided between severe neurosis and mild mental retardation, not necessarily with psychosis.

Acquiring and retaining the member

As we have said, all referrals must come from mental health agencies or professionals, ordinarily physicians or social workers. Most would-be referrals are by telephone, and these calls are taken by a full-time intake secretary, who is not formally trained in the mental health field. In the course of this call she attempts to discern whether the applicant has any characteristics that would cause him to be ineligible, and also to determine whether he has some aspiration for improving his role socially and vocationally (that is, wants something more than just a place to live). She receives an average of three to four telephone inquiries per day.

If the applicant appears to be suitable for Portals, a referral form is sent to the agency wishing to refer him. About thirty percent of these forms are not returned. When one is, the intake secretary, "within three working days," calls the referring person to arrange for the prospective member to attend the next of the weekly orientation meetings.

At the orientation session, to which family members are also invited, the applicant is given a thorough description of the program and its purposes and goals, and he is given an application form to be returned to Portals in the event he decides to apply for membership. About sixty percent of those who attend the orientations submit the application form.

When the application form is received, the intake secretary, again within three working days, telephones the person who referred the applicant to schedule an intake appointment with the professional staff member. During this session there is likely to be an exploration of any ambivalence the applicant may show, some further interpretation of the program, and a statement of what his obligations will be. Whether or not to admit the applicant is usually decided at this session; if the decision is favorable, he at this point becomes counted as part of the caseload.

He is then assigned to one of the two case counselors and also to one of the group counseling meetings and some of the program activities.

The first month is considered an observation period during which a case plan is formulated primarily by the case manager.

The largest group of referrals—26 percent—comes from the county welfare department (Aid to the Disabled), followed by twenty percent from the state hospitals, principally Camarillo. Twelve percent are referred by VA hospitals, eleven percent by general hospital psychiatric units, ten percent by community mental health centers, ten percent by the state vocational rehabilitation agency, seven percent by psychiatrists in private practice, and the remaining few by the probation department and the Youth Authority.

"No-shows." Up to now Portals has not made it a practice to contact those who do not return the application forms in an effort to motivate them to enter the program.

Dropouts. An effort is made to trace those people who simply disappear from the program. But these are few in number, doubtless because the Portals program and the boardinghouse service are in reality a "package deal." In other words, one would have to forego his place of residence as well as his living allowance from welfare if he were to disengage himself entirely from the program.

Attempts are made to reach out through direct intervention by the counselor, boardinghouse operators, and other members. On occasion members are assigned specifically to get nonparticipating members to attend the center. When all these attempts fail the member is usually transferred to a "board-and-care" facility, which provides only room and meals and is not affiliated with any rehabilitation agency.

The program, in general

Portals is best viewed as a socialization/residential program, with as yet little activity in the vocational area. It decided to give up its own residential services in the interest of developing a broader program, but in a very real sense the residential placements are part and parcel of the Portals program. For one thing the three boardinghouses that it uses are exclusively contracted to take Portals members. For another, the Portals staff works directly and closely with the boardinghouse operators, meeting with them weekly and backing them up readily in case of any out-of-the-way development. What takes place at Portals' own facility is almost exclusively in the social adjustment area, and consequently the program, while comprising a unitary socialization/residential resource, is dichotomized, with the boardinghouses offering little other than a place to sleep and eat and Portals offering the socialization program. (With the recently acquired funding from the United Fund, Portals anticipates that it will become able to work with people additional to those living in the boardinghouses.)

Portals is open to members as a sort of informal clubhouse facility and for group counseling only from noon until four p.m. All of the evening activities are programmed. Theoretically members are not free to come in the morning, but a certain percentage come early, attempting to circumvent the rules or to wait around for the opening hour, evidently because they get bored at their boardinghouses, where they do not have anything much to do. Within the staff there is some disagreement about whether Portals should be available as an "open lounge" even for the four hours a day, with some feeling that no one should be permitted to come except for programmed social events, committee meetings, and so on, in the hope that the member will participate at other times in community activities.

A great deal of responsibility for the conduct of members and reprimands for inappropriate behavior lies with the members themselves. Patient government reaches its ultimate in a behavior committee, which has formulated a brief but strictly enforced code of conduct, as follows:

1. There is to be no physical assault on the part of one member against another. Violation leads to automatic termination "or, in extenuating circumstances, suspension or probation."
2. There are to be no threats of physical assault. Violation leads, "according to the seriousness of the offense," to suspension, probation, or termination.
3. No weapons or objects that could be used as weapons are to be in the possession of members. Violation leads to a reprimand and a request for compliance with the rule, and failure to comply may lead to suspension, probation, or termination.
4. There is to be no harassment of a member by any other member that is likely to provoke physical assault, threats, or a need to carry weapons. Violation results in reprimand, suspension, or probation.
5. There must be no destruction or theft of personal property.

It is striking that all of the rules are concerned with assaultive behavior. This might seem strange in view of the effort Portals makes to screen out the potentially aggressive but might be explained partly in terms of the relatively young population and the presence in the program of a certain number of members diagnosed as having character disorders. There have been a number of instances of assaultive behavior, and three members have been terminated for this reason.

Membership on the behavior committee averages about ten. There is strong emphasis on member participation in several other committees: a canteen committee, a welcoming and orientation committee, a grievance committee, a volunteer committee, a reception committee, a Sunday afternoon program committee, a holiday committee, and a newspaper committee. But only about half of the Portals members are participating in the committees.

The house itself prohibits the use of alcohol and any drugs except those prescribed for the members by physicians.

Members ordinarily leave the program to take a job or attend school, and they are then on follow-up status. Their participation is therefore primarily limited to the evening and weekend activities.

Portals sets no time limit for participation, "the length of stay varying according to the needs of each individual." There are periodic reviews to determine what progress each member has made. Occasionally someone who seems to be making none at all is referred to some other resource. The agency does not feel that it has as yet been able to discern any meaningful limits regarding length of participation for various categories of clients. The fact that most Portals members are being supported with funds from the welfare department's Aid to the Disabled program, for which they are indefinitely eligible, may be serving to keep them participating in and dependent on the agency for a longer time than is necessary.

The socialization program

Portals socialization activities can be grouped into two categories: *a*) those that are essentially educative-directive, and *b*) those that are comprised mainly of specific social and recreational activities from which it is hoped that the members, in addition to having something to fill up their time, will learn social skills and become more at ease in interpersonal transactions.

The principal of the educative functions is the mandatory weekly rehabilitation group counseling. Each of the two caseworkers has four groups, each with about ten members. The group is designed to "help the members relate to each other, providing support and mutual guidance." There is also a member council, with an average of twelve members, elected by the total membership. They meet weekly with the staff to consider everyday operations and to discuss the nature and direction of the program activities. At the end of each afternoon there is a meeting of all members who have attended and all of the staff who are on hand, for the purpose of maintaining open communication between members and staff and to deal with any interpersonal problems that have come up.

The "open lounge" program referred to above provides opportunities for members to engage in pool, Ping-pong, cards, parlor games, shuffleboard, and other unscheduled activities. There are also occasional discussion groups and speakers. The lounge program also offers a degree of guidance by volunteers and staff in matters of personal appearance and hygiene and introduces members to the local library, stores, Laundromat, cleaners, and so on. The activities of this portion of the day are seen as "essentially the first stage in introducing the member to the program."

Activities that are more structured and have greater content include:

- A monthly newsletter, whose staff meets twice weekly.

- A weekly supper club, limited to eight persons at a time, intended to teach how to buy and prepare food, and directed by volunteers.

- A weekly bowling session at a nearby bowling alley.

- Body movement classes held for two groups once a week each, as "an introduction to the therapeutic use of body movement that helps to improve body image and body function."

- A weekly trip to some industrial plant, recreational area, historic, educational, or vocational exhibit or facility, with the intent of developing members' interest in the community and teaching them to use public transportation.

- "Multi-interest night," which consists of listening to music, discussing current events, and so on, primarily for members who are working or going to school during the day.

- Sunday afternoon buffet, used to teach members about food preparation and serving; open to current members and alumni. Portals requested the boardinghouses not to serve a Sunday evening meal, as a means of encouraging attendance at the buffet.

- Weekend activities, open to current members and alumni, and consisting of dances, or, with discount tickets, trips to plays, concerts, movies, and sports events.

The residential program

We have mentioned that substantially all of the active Portals members live in one of the three contract boardinghouses. The two we visited were spacious, reasonably pleasant, and moderately well furnished, in a good neighborhood less than a mile from Portals. Across the street from each other, one house is for men members, the other for women, and they are both under the management of the same woman.

Members are housed in rooms for two or three each. While individual members are expected to make their own beds, other cleaning of sleeping rooms and all cleaning of common rooms is done by a domestic. Residents are not expected to help with cooking, or, in general, to do anything in the way of housework except to keep their own rooms reasonably neat and to keep their beds made. Breakfast is served every day, dinner is served except on Sunday, and bag lunches are provided except on Sunday.

For a number of the residents, the boardinghouse manager maintains medications and gives them out at mealtime.

We interviewed the manager of the two boardinghouses mentioned above. They have a capacity of 48, of which 45 places were filled at the time of our visit. She had operated a regular boardinghouse for thirty years prior to entering into the contract with Portals, and the present arrangement has some distinct advantages. For one thing, Portals is able to keep her houses full substantially all of the time. For another, there is never any loss of collection. And there is immediate access to a member of the Portals professional staff in case of trouble, which happens only occasionally.

This woman told us that, all things considered, she has found the Portals members to be no more trouble, and perhaps less, than her tenants when she ran a regular boardinghouse. "The main difference," she said, "is that I used to get people on the way in, and now I get them on the way out."

The vocational program

While Portals has laid plans for a vocational guidance and preparation service that would include individual assessment, occupational information, and counseling, plus follow-up of persons who have entered employment, this aspect of the program was as of the time of our visit still rudimentary.

At a relatively low level of emphasis, there are opportunities during the day to do clerical work such as typing, filing, and addressing envelopes, and members are encouraged to volunteer to help out at such agencies as Red Cross and the mental health association. While such activities can be viewed as useful prevocational steps whereby one learns to attend regularly, to come on time, and to develop a tolerance for the work setting, Portals is well aware that it needs to develop more activities and more structure in this area. When we interviewed a group of members, several of them expressed the hope that Portals would eventually be able to take over the running of a local branch of a short-order food chain (as Fountain House has done in New York). Some of the Portals members who have gone to work have gone out and found their own jobs unassisted; others have been provided referrals by their "community agents" and by members of the board of trustees.

The canteen

The Astrological Bilge Box is the name of the canteen that has been developed in the garage of Portals. Open two afternoons and one evening a week, it offers a variety of goods—cosmetics, clothing, and so on—that have been donated. Members receive scrip by doing maintenance work around the house, serving at the reception desk, telephoning members who do not show up, and volunteering to work at local voluntary agencies. They can exchange this scrip for items from the canteen.

Medication

The considerable majority of Portals members take psychotropic drugs, which are prescribed by the member's physician. Some go to privately practicing psychiatrists, with fees paid under Medi-Cal at the rate of $30 per appointment. (The private psychiatrist who sees a Portals member weekly receives more each month for these four appointments than the boardinghouse manager receives for a month's meals and lodging.) Those who are not eligible for Medi-Cal services obtain medication through the outpatient department of the county mental health program. Those who are clients of the Division of Vocational Rehabilitation receive medication through case service funds.

At one time Portals had a part-time psychiatric consultant, whose services did not prove very useful. We were told that he was extremely reluctant to prescribe medication.

Families

On the grounds of a shortage of staff time, families of members are rarely involved in the Portals program, except that they are invited to the orientation session, at which time they meet separately from the applying group. Ordinarily families are contacted only in critical situations.

Agency and community relationships

Portals appears to enjoy good relationships with a variety of agencies with which it collaborates. The state hospital representative whom we interviewed considered Portals an excellent agency to which to refer a limited number of patients who fall within the Portals target group, most of these to be served for a three-month period under a Division of Vocational Rehabilitation Personal Adjustment Training program. The boardinghouse operators seem to be well pleased with their relationship with Portals.

Portals feels it has had good acceptance from the private medical-psychiatric community but says it has had difficulty with community mental health centers and some public psychiatric interests which it feels "question the value of any nonmedical mental health facility."

There have been no problems with the neighbors or the surrounding community. Portals' present facility, as was the case with the halfway houses, is located in a relatively anonymous intown residential area, and there have been no complaints against it. The agency is very active with the local Chamber of Commerce and several service clubs. There has been a conscious effort to include key people on the board, including a local newspaper publisher.

Portals has been successful in arranging to have new categories of service personnel assigned to it, what with three work-study students from the University of California at Los Angeles and the California State College at Los Angeles, plus two VISTA volunteers (very few mental health programs have been able to arrange for VISTA volunteers to be assigned to them).

Financing

During 1969 Portals operated on a budget of $241,000, a figure that includes not only all the costs of operating the program at its own facility but also includes payments to the boardinghouse operators. The principal sources of these funds were: from the Aid to the Disabled program of the welfare department, 43 percent; from contributions, 20 percent; and from the Division of Vocational Rehabilitation, in fees for clients placed at Portals for the Personal Adjustment Training program, nine percent. The most jarring note in the financial figure is that almost a quarter of the budget—24 percent—had to come from the agency's financial reserves, which represent for the most part the proceeds from the sale of the two halfway houses.

Portals has been, for the sake of survival, married to the boardinghouse program. Portals itself receives the monthly check for each of its welfare members, and in turn writes a check for room and board to the boardinghouse operators and a check to the individual member for his allowance for incidentals. The remaining $63 per member goes toward the cost of operating the socialization and counseling services, and without these funds Portals would not have been able to stay in business.

Consequently, new sources of funds have been urgently sought. Now that it has been approved for funding on the customary "deficit financing" formula of the United Fund, to the anticipated extent of $40,000 per year, the situation will become more favorable. It has also sought a facilities-modernization grant from the Social and Rehabilitation Service of the federal government.

THE FINANCIAL DILEMMA in which Portals found itself as of the time of our visit is a particularly dramatic example of a state of affairs that frequently afflicts voluntary agencies that seek to expand. Dr. Glassman put it as follows:

> Looking at Portals in this period of crisis, one gains an insight into the problems of the small voluntary agency. Rather than being oriented toward providing a certain kind of service, or serving a particular clientele, or meeting a particular need, they must instead orient themselves to a considerable extent towards the available sources of funds. This appears to be necessary both because of their very nature and because they depend on external sources of support. Portals may have to change and/or enlarge its scope and its services simply to survive.

> While these observations may seem cynical, the situation may simply be a corollary of the operations of the free-enterprise market place. Any manufacturer must be aware of where the money is. He manufactures products for which he assumes there will be a market. He does not try to provide services or products for which there is either no demand or no money. Perhaps it is the role of the voluntary agency to provide services in areas where both demand and money are present, and for public agencies to provide services in those areas where only the demand is present.

Outcome

The only outcome study that has been conducted by Portals dealt with its days as a halfway house. It has been in operation on the present basis for a relatively short time, during which it has been in constant financial crisis, with no funds available to provide staff time to carry out an evaluation. Mr. Weinstein and his staff are highly motivated to do so, and this will occur with anticipated improvements in funding. The only criterion thus far available is the rehospitalization rate of persons who have been members at Portals, which in the recent past has been less than twenty percent of those who enter the program.

XI. Hill House
(Mental Health Rehabilitation and Research, Inc.)
Cleveland

HILL HOUSE, A SMALL, WELL-ESTABLISHED CENTER providing service to people who have been hospitalized for major psychiatric illness, came into being through the combined efforts of the Cleveland section of the Council of Jewish Women and the local mental health association. The key figure in this joining of forces was Mrs. Robert Hays, in the late 1950's vice-president both of the Council of Jewish Women and of the mental health association, and still a member of the Hill House board.

The Council of Jewish Women was also responsible for the establishment of Thresholds in Chicago, Council House in Pittsburgh, and Bridgehaven in Louisville. Mrs. Hays described the events and circumstances that led to this interest.

> The various Councils of Jewish Women came to be interested in the rehabilitation of mental patients as a result of the general ground swell of interest in state hospitals during the 1950's. This was largely due to the efforts of some conscientious objectors who were assigned to state hospitals as an alternative to serving in the army; they were appalled by what they saw, and they spread the word about it far and wide. At about the same time some national magazines did major stories on the state hospitals. Another important factor was the experimental efforts with open hospitals starting in the early 1950's, and of course the advent of the new drug therapies in the mid-1950's.

The Cleveland Mental Health Association appointed a Committee on Rehabilitation of Discharged Patients, whose report, published in 1957, estimated that approximately one thousand of the four thousand patients discharged to the Cleveland area each year by the state hospitals required a broad variety of rehabilitation services. The Council of Jewish Women, spurred by this report, then determined to establish a center providing mainly opportunities for social activities. "But we soon decided that it was risky for a nonprofessional organization such as ours to attempt to run a social agency, and so we teamed up with the mental health association," Mrs. Hays told us.

Thus the Council of Jewish Women and the mental health association jointly appointed a group known as the Cleveland Halfway Center Advisory Committee, which carried out a survey in 1959. The findings further documented the need for a variety of services to people recently discharged from mental hospitals. This committee made several recommendations about the form that such a service should in their opinion take.

• It should be administratively and physically separate from any other institution.

• It should be located in the community.

• It should be transitional and not terminal.

• It should establish priorities whereby those who need the service most will have the highest priority.

• It should incorporate research efforts into all of the service components.

Subsequently it was decided that neither the mental health association nor the Council of Jewish Women would operate the service, but instead that they would provide support and impetus for the creation of an independent agency. By December 1960, with the aid of some small "seeding grants," funds became available to hire an executive director, who set up an office in a room rented from the mental health association. Three months later the new Hill House moved to the first of three contiguous buildings which it now occupies, and the executive director plus a secretary carried out the program.

In the meantime a research-demonstration grant had been sought from the National Institute of Mental Health. In mid-1961 Hill House was notified that a five-year grant had been approved, whereupon professional staff were recruited and a full-time service program begun. Seventeen psychiatric facilities in the Cleveland area—four state hospitals, two Veterans Administration hospitals, eight general hospitals with psychiatric units, and three private psychiatric hospitals—were told about the new social rehabilitation service and invited to refer patients to it.

Philosophy, purposes, and policy

At the heart of the Hill House theory of rehabilitation is the belief that the major problem facing the recently released psychiatric patient is making the transition from the passive, dependent, and restricted role of the patient to the independent, competitive, and complex role of the citizen and that the more roles in which the former patient develops some competence, the less likelihood of his future rehospitalization. From this belief comes a conception of five steps in the resocialization process.

- To make the patient aware of alternatives available to him.
- To define the alternatives in terms of the quantity and quality of expectations associated with each alternative.
- To motivate the patient to want to occupy some of the alternative positions of which he has been made aware.
- To teach him the specific acts associated with each alternative in relation to opposing alternatives.
- To have the patient learn the patterned sequences of acts associated with each alternative he chooses.

"In actuality," says a Hill House research report, "the steps are not discrete but overlap considerably. To effect successful resocialization, it may even be necessary that they overlap."

In determining the type and nature of services that the former mental patient needs, Hill House delineates some aspects of the hospital environment thought to influence the nature of the posthospital program: *a*) the patient's loss of personal identity, resulting in role diffusion in a strange living arrangement; *b*) the inconsistencies of role expectations between the hospital and the community; *c*) the patient's feeling of total abandonment and role loss.

The essence of the transitional problem from hospital to community living is seen in terms of various ways in which the hospital's role expectations are inconsistent with community expectations. "These are two quite distinct and different social systems, each with its own set of values," a research report states.

> For instance, it is not unusual for a patient to perform with a high degree of social ability in the controlled, sheltered environment of a hospital, seemingly quite independently. Yet, it is conceivable that he seeks a very dependent role in which he literally surrounds his environment with protective and supportive devices: seeking staff commendation, doing errands for others, participating in the least anxiety-producing programs. In the community, he wouldn't have a chance.

Akin to this is the belief that hospitals reward patients for achieving an emotional role (stability, conformity, etc.) but not for achieving an instrumental role, as in working at a job in the hospital. If the former mental patient is to achieve independent living, he must acquire five capabilities: *a*) the ability to get along with other people, *b*) the ability to perform adequately and to accept his role in a family unit, *c*) the ability to work and to become self-reliant, *d*) a desire for self-improvement, and *e*) the use of appropriate community resources.

While the total social rehabilitation program must be geared to the patient's need for social contacts and to the level of his ability to function socially, Hill House believes that continual demands must be made of the member to participate in the program as a responsible adult. "We have learned to articulate these expectations in terms that have meaning to the patient: to make new friends, to learn to get along with others, to get over shyness, to talk about his problems, to take responsibility voluntarily for such group tasks as publishing a newspaper, preparing meals, and manning a refreshment stand."

The foregoing concepts are based on certain major assumptions, the first of which is that *expectations are a major determinant of behavior changes,* and the more explicit the expectations, the greater the stimulus for change will be. The patient's release from the hospital is viewed by Hill House as indicating that he is capable of at least some level of independent functioning. The intake workers who offer Hill House services to the patients while they are still in hospital impart this message: "You will be leaving the hospital soon because your doctor feels that you are well enough to live in the community. But you may not have an easy time getting back to the routine of daily living, your routine may need in some respects to be modified. Your doctor and Hill House feel that participating in the Hill House program will help you to get readjusted to living outside again." It is also made clear to the prospective member that Hill House is a place where he will be expected to interact with other people; thus the purpose of his participating is put in such terms as "making new friends" or "preparing for a job."

A second assumption is that *improvement in behavior occurs when the program emphasizes the assets and emotional strengths of the patient.* The program of Hill House provides group experiences at several levels, and a given member may participate at more than one level at a given time or may move up or down from one level to another.

A third assumption is that *changes in behavior can occur within a given time period,* and the setting of a limit may indeed influence the rate of change.

The principal method of attempting to support the patient is social group work, designed "to build on current ego strengths and improve role performance of patients in the family and in the community, including social peer and work relationships." Hill House defines social group work as "a method of professional social work practice."

It is generally agreed among social workers that the purpose of group work is to help individuals enhance their social functioning through purposeful group experiences, and to cope more effectively with their personal, group, or community problems. According to Gisela Knopka there are two basic assumptions that underlie social group work. *1*) Next to biological necessities, one's deepest longings are to be loved and to be important to someone. Human beings have not only the basic need to be loved, but the capacity and strength to love in return. It is not infrequent, however, that circumstances in one's life may prevent, suppress, diminish, or make it very difficult to maintain this capacity. And *2*), individuals achieve healthy development through a healthy and appropriate group life.

The group program at Hill House is consequently patterned on the following assumptions: *a*) that patients need to belong to and be accepted by others; *b*) that small group experiences can influence the individual's acceptance of values and standards of behavior to which the group and its members subscribe; *c*) that learning to get along with others becomes meaningful only as enhanced opportunities are provided for voluntary participation and decision making within the group; *d*) that learning to understand oneself is an experience that develops only through reality testing, identification, and self-appraisal; and *e*) that a community-based program for those with mental disorders must conform to the minimum expectations of society.

While all Hill House members are scheduled to participate in social group work activities, the majority, either some of the time or much of the time, are also seen individually by the five members of the professional staff. During the early period of membership these individual contacts typically focus on immediate practical problems, such as arranging for the care of young children, difficulties of living with relatives, getting from home to Hill House and back, and money problems. For patients who have been attending Hill House over a longer period of time the individual sessions are more likely to focus on plans for getting a job or on motivational problems about continuing to participate in the program.

The social structure of Hill House, particularly as evidenced in its group programs, incorporates certain "prescribed social norms and expectations" drawn from the minimal social norms that non-mentally ill adults are expected to meet. These include:

• Regular attendance. Hill House is concerned that irregular attendance will probably lead to a gradual decline in involvement followed by complete withdrawal. Furthermore, an appreciable number of its patients in past years have attended so irregularly that their participation was essentially meaningless.

• Active involvement, including a prohibition of total passiveness. Says a Hill House report, "It is one thing to work with a patient at his level of functioning; it is another matter to encourage, by total permissiveness, the symptoms of his illness."

• Personal cleanliness and appropriate dress. Here the demand is implicit except where lack of conformity requires that it be made explicit.

The program has been designed and refined with a view toward the preferred Hill House client: the person with a functional psychosis, in most cases schizophrenia or a major depression, who, in addition to his history of illness, is evaluated as needing a socialization experience that will support his adjustment to living in the community. In the interest of establishing boundaries intended to enhance the probability of successful outcome with the primary target population, Hill House has established certain exclusions. Because the program is directed toward helping members to assume adult roles and responsibilities, generally persons under twenty years of age are not accepted. "On a few occasions we tried younger persons, but our expectations of adult behavior were inconsistent with their need to work out adolescent conflicts," we were told.

Persons with organic diagnosis are also generally not accepted, principally because they are felt to require more supervision and control than Hill House is prepared to provide; the older persons with organic disorder are thought to be better served by "golden age" groups, while the younger ones are felt not to have adequate potential for conscious behavior change. For much the same reason the severely retarded are not accepted. A final category of exclusion is the person whose primary diagnosis is alcoholism or drug addiction, because such persons have not seemed to be able to maintain any regularity of attendance.

All of the foregoing statement of philosophy and purpose is translated into a set of practical persuasions about how to operate a rehabilitation center for the functionally ill adult client.

• The program should be physically and administratively separate from the hospital (or any other institution), and should be "community based" in a location easily accessible by public transportation. It should be housed in a building that looks like an ordinary residence.

• In addition to his participation in the rehabilitation program, the patient should be involved in other activities and have other responsibilities, such as attending a vocational training program, looking for a job, attending church, and carrying out such everyday responsibilities as cleaning house, cooking, shopping, and taking care of children.

• The program should be directed by trained professionals who are skilled in helping people who have problems in personal relationships. The staff should know how to help people use various services and resources in the community, and should be continuously involved with the hospitals and other agencies that refer patients to them.

• The program should encourage and develop opportunities for regular use of and involvement in the programs and facilities of such agencies as the YMCA, YWCA, settlement houses, and churches.

• The program should be transitional in nature, and not terminal, and therefore should set a time limit for active participation.

Hill House presents a summary statement of its philosophy of rehabilitation: the more difficult the rehabilitation job, the more involvement is necessary before there is any observable improvement.

Auspices and administration

Hill House was incorporated in April 1960 as a nonprofit Ohio corporation, under the official name of Mental Health Rehabilitation and Research, Inc. There is a thirty-member board of trustees, consisting of leading laymen in the community, who serve three-year terms. None of the board members represent the mental health professions; however, there is a 25-member professional advisory committee, whose members are sometimes invited to serve on committees of the board of trustees. Various of the five Hill House professional staff members are also sometimes invited to serve on board committees. In the recent past it has become the practice to elect some of the more experienced volunteers from the treatment program to the board.

We interviewed Robert J. Asman, an attorney who was president of the board. In another city he had been counsel for the commission that licenses physicians and in this capacity had come to know a number of psychiatrists working at the local mental hospital, and had handled cases for them. He said:

> The whole area of mental illness interested me as a result of these contacts and experiences. When I came to Cleveland the Hill House concept was new to me. It was an exciting idea to do something useful for people being released from mental institutions, who might be dumped out into the world without a suitable place to go, with families not ready to accept them back, or who may have been partly the cause of the patient's problems in the first place. I saw that Hill House was trying to provide a refuge in which they could find the

kind of atmosphere that would help them to function independently in the community. In my present job I get around the community a lot, and I tell lawyers and businessmen about Hill House, and they ask me whether Cleveland needs more Hill Houses. I tell them that I think it does.

Location and physical plant

Hill House is situated in a series of three separate but contiguous wooden houses which were formerly family residences and are now rented from a single owner. They consist of three rooms each on the first and second floors. The program began in only one of the buildings but was fortunately able to acquire the second and the third as their former tenants vacated. At present one building is used as the center for the activity groups of members, with social rooms, lounges, an adequate kitchen, a dining area, and a small meeting room.

The furnishings are modest and comfortable. A second building is used for office space for the staff, volunteers, and students. The third building is set aside for the research activities, described later, providing offices for the research staff and space to house the research equipment. A fourth contiguous building will soon be acquired to provide additional office and program space.

The buildings are located in a mixed residential and commercial neighborhood that appears to be heading slightly downward. The street is a heavily traveled main thoroughfare.

The four houses, of similar architecture, are further unified by being painted the same shade of bluish gray. They stand out from neighboring buildings because their color and style suggest a coherence in a jumbled strip development.

One could argue equally for and against the four-building arrangement. On the one hand, the separate houses can be said to fragment staff, program, and research. On the other, one can maintain that the separate houses make possible a desirable specialization among the program's major components. In either case, Hill House is not happy with its present facilities and plans to acquire a larger and more integrated physical plant in the future. One recent effort was defeated as a result of a protest from residents living near the proposed new facility, near the university, who did not want mental patients coming into their neighborhood and resented further encroachment by institutions. A portion of the funds needed for a new building has been raised, and Hill House will attempt to find a large, homelike edifice. Future plans also include the addition to the program of a temporary sheltered residential component, which will be located elsewhere.

There are no satellite facilities, and out-of-house activities are limited to *a*) outings and events planned by Hill House members and *b*) a limited amount of placing selected members in the social programs of the YMCA, the YWCA, a Jewish community center, and settlement houses, while they continue to participate in the program offered at Hill House. Also, regular use is made of YMCA, YWCA, Music School Settlement, and a commercial bowling alley as part of the ongoing group programs of Hill House.

The staff

The professional staff at Hill House is small: an executive director, who holds a master's degree in social work; two senior social workers, one a group worker, the other a caseworker; an additional group worker and caseworker; a part-time research director, who is a psychologist; and a part-time research associate, who is a sociologist. In contrast to some of the other rehabilitation centers that we visited, Hill House has consistently employed only professionals for its treatment program, and all but two of these have been social workers. Absent from the staff are the young social reformers, the stabilized and reformed alcoholics, the VISTA volunteers, who at their best add color and verve to a treatment facility. At Hill House one experiences, by contrast, the impact of a functional social work orientation, with a concomitant great sense of order and classification. From the standpoint of training, the small Hill House staff seem more experienced and more technologically competent than that of some other facilities that we visited. All of the staff at Hill House evidenced that they are willing to undertake functions outside their formal training, and often do so. Morale seemed high; the staff's identification with the agency and its members seemed positive.

One reason for the emphasis on trained staff is the director's conviction that the skills of social work "are necessary to understand the levels of socialization and role expectations. Furthermore, it is important to be able to distinguish between healthy and pathological behavior; the same act can be a sign of growth in one patient, of regression in another."

The director, Henry Tanaka, prior to coming to Hill House had worked for seven years at a state hospital, where he was responsible for group services. Principally he worked at developing predischarge groups and programs in conjunction with various community agencies, principally neighborhood-based YMCA's and YWCA's. "I suppose this is one of the reasons I became interested in what Hill House proposed to do," he told us. "I came to Hill House through an invitation from an advisory committee on halfway centers, to help develop some ideas for community programs."

The senior caseworker had also been at a nearby state hospital, for about three years, following which he spent two years on the staff of an inquiry commission investigating commitments to state hospitals. He became acquainted through this work with the Hill House director, who invited him to join the staff of the young agency. The senior group worker also had been employed at a psychiatric hospital, where she was director of group work. There she had known Mr. Tanaka, who invited her to join the Hill House staff. "I had been promoted into an administrative position, but that was not really what I wanted, and I left largely to get back to a position in which I could spend most of my time with patients."

The senior group worker, who works three-quarters time, is the leader of several of the fifteen activity groups, her share at a given time ranging from three to six groups. At the time of our visit she was heading four groups, each having from five to twelve members. In addition, she was seeing five patients for individual sessions, rarely on a regular basis, usually on a crisis basis. The group worker who reports to her headed up three groups—the Monday afternoon "lounge program" designed for members functioning at a fairly low level, a current events discussion group, and a weekly evening social group which includes preparation and serving of dinner. Most of the participants in the latter two groups are working either part time or, less often, full time.

The senior caseworker and the caseworker who reports to him are principally involved in recruiting patients, contacting them while they are still in hospital, acquainting them with the Hill House program, and urging them to become participants. The senior caseworker makes regular visits to two state hospitals and occasionally, on request, to the Veterans Administration Hospital or to the psychiatric sections of private general hospitals. He also supervises a graduate student and is responsible for the prevocational work programs described below. The caseworker who reports to him makes twice-weekly visits to the nearest state hospital, located only about a mile from Hill House, and in addition to promoting Hill House membership to patients about to be discharged, she also brings some of them by automobile to Hill House for a special orientation group designed for all prospective members. She also sees ten members in regular weekly counseling sessions and provides counseling to still other members as it appears to be needed.

There are weekly scheduled meetings of the staff. When important developments occur between staff meetings, the small size of the staff and their ready accessibility to each other makes immediate handling a simple matter. At staff meetings there are discussions of new admissions, of plans for discharge from Hill House, and a consideration of any unusual cases or problems.

One member of the staff described the philosophy of the program and of each staff person as "present oriented, reality oriented, goal directed, and fairly directive in approach." She said that this orientation was much at odds with the strongly Freudian orientation that all five staff members had received in their training at a nearby university. "It was experience on the job that redirected us," one staff member said. "The agency's philosophy seems to be well accepted by the agencies we deal with, and we make decisions about our own and other staff members' clients with a good deal of confidence that we understand each other. If I make a mistake it is more likely to be as a result of lack of information, not because of any discrepancy in our objectives."

Volunteers

Hill House has made substantial use of volunteers in its treatment program from the earliest days. At the time of our visit there were fifteen volunteers participating in various social group activities. They were used in some cases as group leaders and in others as assistants to staff group workers. As independent group leaders they have headed up arts and crafts, bowling, and cooking groups. Volunteers are recruited through three community groups that recruit and screen applicants: the central volunteer bureau of the Welfare Federation, the Junior League, and the Council of Jewish Women. A few volunteers approach the program as a result of some publicity it has received, a few others are referred by existing volunteers.

All volunteers report to one or the other of the two social group workers, with the frequency of contact depending on the qualifications of the particular volunteer. Volunteers also attend a training session that meets once a month except during the summer.

The executive director carries out the initial interview with the volunteer applicant. Then the group worker who will work with or supervise the volunteer oversees her orientation.

Volunteers are expected to meet each week with their assigned groups and usually are not accepted unless they can commit themselves to the assignment for at least a year.

During our visit we interviewed one of the volunteers and then joined the Thursday evening dinner group with which she works. We were impressed with the poise, competence, and ease with which she went about her assignment. She told us of the way in which she became associated with Hill House.

> The Junior League suggested an assignment at Hill House. I hadn't had any experience with mentally ill people, and I didn't know what to expect—whether they'd be sitting around listlessly or weaving back and forth, whether they could carry on any kind of intelligent conversation, whether it would be all right for me to ask about their problems. Well, in the beginning one boy asked me whether I got angry; he said I was a normal person, and he wanted to know if normal people got angry. So I began to think about how hospitals try to subdue anger, so that this boy was afraid of his own anger and didn't know whether he could show it without ending up in the hospital again. A great many of the questions they have asked me really had much more than the manifest content. At the end of the meeting I tell the group worker about the questions that seem to be significant.

The members

Eligibility. Any resident of the metropolitan Cleveland area who is twenty years of age or older and who has been hospitalized for a major mental illness for at least one month during the year prior to his application to Hill House is eligible for membership, without respect to "racial, cultural, religious, and socioeconomic background." Those who were hospitalized but discharged more than a year prior to application are accepted on a selective basis, even though "their needs were more of a preventive rather than rehabilitative nature."

General characteristics. A research report based on 442 patients who became active members of Hill House during its first five and a half years states that the members can be characterized as unmarried chronic schizophrenics between the ages of twenty and forty, a little more than half of them with at least some high school education and about a fifth with post-high school education. Of persons who participated in the program during 1969, approximately one third (32 percent) were men, two thirds (68 percent) women. About three quarters of the 60 men (77 percent) were between the ages of 21 and 40, while three fifths (59 percent) of the 127 women were within these same age limits. The distribution by race is approximately that of the patients in state hospitals serving Cleveland, namely, two thirds white, one third Negro.

As for place of residence during the time they participate in Hill House activities, more than half of the men active in the program during 1969 lived with their parents, while two fifths of the women were living either with their husbands or their children. Specifically:

	Men	Women
Living with parents	53%	15%
Living with spouses and/or children	8	40
Living with other than above	23	11
Living alone	15	34

The great majority of patients are unemployed at the time they enter the Hill House program, but a considerable number find part-time or full-time work while continuing to participate in Hill House activities. For a total of 60 men and 127 women active in the program during 1969, the vocational situation was as follows:

	Men	Single women	Married women
Competitively employed full time	31%	22%	6%
Competitively employed part time	15	11	19
Employed in sheltered setting full time	3	4	0
Employed in sheltered setting part time	2	3	6
Unemployed	23	19	6
Not in labor market*	26	42	63

*These are persons on VA and Social Security disability pensions, single women with children, and older persons not able or planning to work.

Diagnoses. We have mentioned that the modal, or typical, Hill House member came to the program after having been hospitalized with a diagnosis of schizophrenia. For 116 cases activated in 1969 (97 new cases, 19 reopened cases), almost three quarters (72 percent) had a diagnosis of schizophrenia; an additional six percent represented various other forms of psychosis; 17 percent were nonpsychotic, mostly schizoid personalities, neurotic depressions, and passive-aggressive personalities; and for five percent the diagnosis while in hospital was not known.

The senior caseworker told us that Hill House members have changed over the years in respect of treatment history. "When we started, there was a great concentration of long-term chronic patients, but now we are getting fewer and fewer of those. These days many of our patients have been in and out of hospital many times, with a relatively brief stay during each episode of hospitalization."

A psychiatrist who works at the nearby state hospital and who refers many of the Hill House members said that Hill House is often resorted to by former hospital patients who, but for the availability of the Hill House program, would doubtless require rehospitalization. When asked her greatest problem for her discharged chronic patients, she replied, "Seeing that they take their medication."

Sources of referrals

The predominance of schizophrenic members can be attributed largely to the sources of referrals. Of 183 persons who entered the program during 1968, more than three quarters (77 percent) came from state hospitals; another 15 percent came from general hospital psychiatric sections, three percent from psychiatrists in private practice, and five percent from a variety of other sources.

A psychiatrist from a state hospital told us that she bases referral to Hill House mainly on the chronicity of the case. "Also, I refer patients who are alone and likely to be lonely," she said. "For example, I had a woman patient who had been hospitalized twice, her husband was in the process of divorcing her, and she was inadequate to take care of the children. She really had nobody. She was leaving the hospital to go out and live in a rented room. She was fragile and very obsessive-compulsive, bewildered about what to do and what was going to happen to her. I thought if she could latch on to something like Hill House it might make all the difference, and I really don't think she could have made it without the help of Hill House."

Like day hospitals, outpatient clinics, and most other mental health facilities that provide less than 24-hour care, Hill House has had some problems both in maintaining a steady flow of referrals and in persuading the prospective member to accept the services offered. In the matter of referrals, the number has fallen off several times over the years, mainly because of administrative changes and reorganizations within the hospitals that refer the majority of patients. Hill House staff responded by increasing the frequency of contacts with the hospitals' treatment staff—"in general, beating the drum." At one particular point when there was a paucity of referrals, Hill House staff members conducted interviews with 74 state hospital doctors and social workers in order to determine their views about aftercare needs of recently released patients. These people estimated that about a third of their patients needed social rehabilitation services, but only about two fifths of this group were receiving them. They explained the unmet needs in terms of the shortage of hospital personnel, low patient motivation, and lack of posthospital facilities and services. The Hill House staff thus concluded that they must make greater efforts to overcome the low motivation of their prospective members.

As for the "refusal rate," Hill House has found by experimentation that it is apt to be very high when the initial contacts are not within the critical period prior to hospital release, and fairly low when there are planned efforts to acquaint prospective members with the program shortly before they leave the hospital. Said Mr. Tanaka, "When we began to concentrate great effort on the two-week period prior to release, plus the first week after release, the refusal rate dropped from a high of 70 percent to the present level of about 35 percent. This three-week period seems to be absolutely critical. Patients are started in our three-session orientation program two weeks prior to discharge, and thus the final session comes during the week after discharge. By then, we hope that each one will have moved into at least one of our regular group activities."

The intake procedure

The visits to patients while they are still in the hospital, and the orientation sessions at Hill House, are considered a major part of the intake procedure; in addition to attempting to interest the prospective member, these sessions also serve as a preliminary investigating period to determine whether the individual meets all of the eligibility criteria, what his needs are, and whether the particular services available at Hill House seem likely to benefit him. A prospect does not become identified as a client until after he has attended the second meeting, and even then the staff feel that a month of regular participation is really needed to determine whether and in what way a given individual will fit into Hill House activities. This process helps to determine whether a given individual who meets the stated formal eligibility criteria is likely to meet the minimal functional requirements, such as coming to the program regularly and unescorted. Bizarre or disruptive behavior, which is minimal, is dealt with in the groups or in individual counseling. If such behavior persists, other available community resources are consulted.

The prospective member's first relationship is with one of the two caseworkers, functioning as intake workers. Once a new member has become active in one or more of the groups, his needs are re-evaluated at a staff conference; if it appears that he will need regular and continued individual counseling, then he remains in the caseload of the

caseworker. Most of the members, however, need only supportive counseling, which is given by the caseworker or group worker who has the
best relationship.

The intake worker and the new member together decide which group
or groups the new member will enter initially. If the intake worker is in
doubt about the suitability of a particular one of the fifteen groups, she
is likely to consult one of the group workers.

None of the program elements are compulsory per se, but it is anticipated that each member will attend at least one group on a reasonably
regular basis. There is no maximum limit on participation, although the
modal number of groups per patient is three, relatively few have as many
as five, and none more than that number.

Aggressive follow-up of absentees and dropouts results from the Hill
House philosophy that it should not only serve the motivated member
but also motivate the unmotivated. Regularity of attendance is constantly stressed and members are expected to call when unable to attend
scheduled appointments or groups.

Those who have been visited in the hospital and/or brought to the
orientation sessions but who do not show up after discharge from the
hospital are sent a letter inviting them to Hill House. Those who have
attended for a period of time and then drop out are contacted by
telephone or letter by the staff person felt to have the most significant
relationship with them. On rare occasions home visits have been made
to dropouts. Occasionally a fellow member may express interest in a
person who has stopped attending and will be encouraged to call the
absentee.

Dropouts, as well as persons who have left the program by mutual
agreement, are free to re-enter if the staff believes a further period at
Hill House would be useful.

The program

General. The Hill House program has been, by design, limited essentially to providing socialization experiences plus individual counseling as
indicated. There is a limited effort to help patients prepare for and find
either competitive or sheltered job placements, and scarcely any activity
in providing or helping to find sheltered residential placements.

It is important to realize that, in contrast to Fountain House and
Horizon House, members are by no means encouraged to use the facilities as any kind of clubhouse. They are welcome only for scheduled
group or individual appointments, and the staff gently dissuade those
who want to make Hill House a home away from home.

In the recent past, at the request of several members, a members council was organized. Its purposes are *a*) to help orient new members, *b*) to improve communications with staff, *c*) to plan weekend activities (Hill House is not open on Saturdays and Sundays), *d*) to plan social events, *e*) to assist members who are preparing to leave Hill House, and *f*) to provide a forum for discussing various problems of the members. The council, with nine and sometimes more members, is not at any given time necessarily representative of the different levels or groups of the Hill House program. Any person who wants to attend the weekly meetings of the council may do so, and thereby become a member. The members elect officers quarterly. Two of the members serve on the program committee of the board of trustees.

Socialization. The fifteen different groups constitute the area on which the Hill House staff focuses most of its effort and concern. The groups are graded according to three levels. The lowest of these, including such activities as arts and crafts, social skills, bowling and other sports, is seen as the *activity level.* The intermediate, consisting of task-oriented activities such as preparing meals, publishing a newspaper, or planning social programs, is known as the *social level.* The highest level, including such groups as play reading, council meetings, and problem discussion groups, is known as the *discussion level.*

These groups are also conceptualized in dichotomies of *verbal* vs. *nonverbal* and *structured* vs. *nonstructured.* The intake worker attempts as described above to identify the appropriate level for the new member. If the level proves too high or too low he can be moved to a group at another level.

The activity groups make minimal social demands, and it is recognized and accepted that group members may be socially immobile and isolated. Verbal communication is often at the simplest level. Activities are highly individual and concrete, thus providing a structure in which the asocial behavior can be tolerated in an unthreatening environment. In the crafts group, for example, a member may prefer to be totally removed emotionally from others by concentrating on his own project. But new and more demanding roles begin to emerge as the members learn to share equipment, compare one another's work, or help with the serving of coffee. "In effect," a Hill House report states, "the member learns or relearns social skills—how to meet the simplest social demands of being with a group. In the bowling group, for example, the member learns the simple courtesy of taking his turn and of respecting the bowler on his right. This serves as a constant reminder that his own enjoyment is dependent upon his respect for others."

The social groups impose increased social demands, and there is little provision for isolated activity. Such tasks as preparing a meal, publishing a newspaper, and organizing an evening of social activity require involvement of other members in planning and carrying out assignments, making decisions and choices. It is a group norm not to tolerate social withdrawal. Nonconforming behavior is disapproved and is "handled by means of social rejection, scapegoating, delegating of the least desirable tasks." Thus, social groups are seen as providing a wider base for social interaction, with greater social demands.

The discussion groups present intensified social demands, since each member is expected to share his personal problems and to react to the problems presented by others. In these groups there are no concrete activities, except those such as films that might be used to stimulate a discussion of vocational planning problems. Those chosen for discussion groups are the members who have demonstrated a reasonable degree of comfort in their social relationships and the ability to talk and listen to others.

Such a first-level group as the Friday morning crafts group is described as structured and nonverbal. The group leader uses the activity to help the patients achieve such basic social skills as coming regularly, coming on time, coming appropriately dressed, and learning to say hello on arriving and goodbye on departing. Near the end of each session, the leader attempts to involve the members in a discussion.

For a second-level group such as the Thursday evening supper club, a group worker purchases the food during the day, since most of the members work. They arrive about 5:00 p.m. and thereafter divide up the duties of preparing and cooking the food, serving it, and then cleaning up. After dinner there is a variety of recreational activities and informal discussions.

An evaluation of each patient's progress takes place at the end of his first, sixth, and tenth month of membership. At these points the staff consider whether the member is involved in groups appropriate to his level, and it may be decided to encourage a particular member to join a higher-level group; in doing so he need not relinquish the lower-level group, and it is not uncommon for members to be simultaneously attending groups at two or even three different levels. The movement back and forth is of course not regular and there is sometimes regression as well as progression within the membership of a particular group.

None of the groups include "confrontation" or "encounter" in the usual contemporary sense of these terms, nor are they designed to increase the member's insight into his psychodynamics or the nature of his illness. The staff hope and seem to feel that the group experience is "relevant" with respect both to relationship and content; they hope that the relationship experiences are generalizable to the members' experiences in the community at large, and that the content (as in a current events group) will help the members to focus on the outside world rather than primarily on themselves.

Out of the members council had grown an "alumni group" of Hill House members, consisting of those who had moved up to the highest level and those who had terminated altogether. Called "Operation Crossover," this group came about because of the termination of a particular member. As one member of "Operation Crossover" told us:

> When Jerry was being terminated, he felt so ill at ease about leaving and not having anything to go to that we asked him if he would come to the members council just for visits to make him feel better. We soon decided that we really shouldn't allow the "graduates" to keep coming to council on visitor status, so another member said, Why don't we start a group of our own?

The 25-member group holds monthly meetings at a church and sponsors monthly social events. Among the ten members we met with, there seemed to be a sense of accomplishment that they had coalesced into a successful social club "without having to have a social worker with us." One of the members said proudly, "We have almost perfect attendance at every meeting, and even Hill House can't boast of that!"

Vocational. Hill House does not as yet provide any formal vocational services of such types as sheltered workshop, transitional employment, job sampling, or job placement. Its activities are limited to the prevocational area, consisting primarily of *a*) four "work experience" projects and *b*) some counseling and guidance about how to look for and apply for a job.

The short-term work experience projects consist of engaging members in maintenance and clerical projects within Hill House and a transitional secretarial office position at the Cleveland Mental Health Association. The focus is on "establishing or stabilizing basic work habits and work-related interpersonal relationships." The participants are paid from $.75 to $1.25 per hour, and typically work six to nine hours per week. Examples of the particular kinds of work assignments are yard work, housekeeping tasks, and collating and typing. Relatively few Hill House members participate in these projects, rarely more than five at a time.

A summer work experience project during the past several years has involved from six to eight members in operating a concession stand at a suburban public swimming pool open six afternoons a week. Members work in pairs. They are entirely responsible for the project, except for bookkeeping and buying supplies. They are paid ninety cents per hour plus a share of the profits.

Beyond these particular projects, Hill House concern with finding and getting jobs is limited principally to advice and role playing. Some discussion groups go through practice runs of filling out job applications and of job interviews. For the most part members are expected to locate their own jobs, sometimes through the state employment office but more often through classified ads in the daily papers. Staff members will occasionally help a reticent person to go through the classifieds.

This limited activity in the vocational area seems to stem in part from the structured, ordered philosophy of Hill House. A research report states:

> Not infrequently the new member presents a picture of being totally overwhelmed by his problems and frustrated by the lack of movement. Some believe that a job will solve all their problems. Helping the member sort out his problems and place them in some realistic order of importance is . . . a job for individual counseling.

In one of our interviews a staff member expressed the belief that if a person is qualified to hold a job he should also be qualified to locate it and be hired for it.

But to some extent it seems probable that the limited vocational effort is a jurisdictional matter. Hill House is a member of the United Appeal in Cleveland and thereby has particular stipulated services to provide, among which vocational services are at least not primary and are assigned to other community agencies. However, Hill House and fellow agencies recognize the need for more collaborative efforts to provide intensive and extensive vocational service. Hill House sees the need to add another dimension to the spectrum of vocational services which would be more specifically geared to the needs of former mental patients.

Residential. Again by original intent and design, Hill House does not provide residential service to its members, either under its own aegis or through collaboration with other agencies. There are no halfway houses in Cleveland. The need for group residential placements was, however, expressed several times by staff members, and particularly eloquently by the Hill House members themselves. We asked the eight members with whom we met what one component they would most like to see added to the Hill House program, and all except one mentioned "a live-in facility." Said one member:

A lot of the people that come out of the hospital really don't have anywhere to go, and a lot of them room with private families, in very uncomfortable situations. Sometimes they're taken advantage of. This arrangement is a step backward, not a step forward.

Said one of the male members who was in his mid-twenties:

I live at home, yet I crave so much to live with people my own age. I always have, and I never had the opportunity, and I think it would help me a great deal. I want the friendships that I don't have, that I could have much better if I were in a halfway house.

Said one of the women in her early twenties:

At this point, when I'm living alone, I certainly wouldn't want to go *back* to a halfway house. But I think that my "down time" when I had to go back to the hospital would have been cut in half if we had had a live-in residence to go to instead.

Various purposes of a residential facility were mentioned. Some members and staff were interested in a "traditional" halfway house designed to provide residence during a transitional period from hospital to community; others wanted a "crisis facility" where members could come to stay briefly at times of particular trouble or distress, in the belief thereby that rehospitalization might be averted.

Since the time of our visit a committee made up of board, staff, and Hill House members has been studying the feasibility of a transitional housing program. It is envisioned as a physically separate house for a maximum of ten to twelve residents, largely self-supporting, and with minimal staffing.

Families of members

As part of the intake procedure the caseworkers evaluate whether there seems to be a probability that the relatives of members would help in the rehabilitation plan, whether any significant family member might be available in time of need, and whether it is Hill House or some other agency that is most appropriate for working with the family. In actuality, there is little contact with families, in part because many of the members do not have families or have families that will not collaborate with Hill House, and in part because there is not adequate staff time. There is direct contact with families in forty percent or fewer of the cases, mostly with parents of single members. Some members who are working toward independence from families do not want to have their families involved.

In the past a discussion group was started for adult family members, but it "turned out to be diverse in constituency and had some difficulty in achieving focus." At another time a ten-session series for parents of younger members was tried, with limited success; "attendance was clearly related to parents' dissatisfaction with their child's role performance."

Relatives are invited to certain special social events, and with advance clearance may attend certain group meetings, but rarely do.

Home visits are occasionally made, usually because of some crisis within the family, or because a member is unable to get away from family responsibilities.

Agency and community relationships

We have mentioned that Hill House was unable to purchase a particular building because of the opposition of residents living near it. This came about only in part because of the stigma of mental illness; opposition to a development plan was also involved. At its existing location there have been no problems of community relationships. The neighborhood is relatively anonymous and highly urban, and there do not seem to be very extensive "neighborly" transactions.

Relationships with the professional community appear to be well established and well operating. Hill House staff feel that many of the professionals know about them and understand what their services, purposes, and intended clientele are. But there is continual need to interpret the program. Referrals are now generally adequate in number and almost always appropriate in nature.

Hill House is a contracting agency with the county mental health board, under an arrangement described below under Finances. Recently Hill House negotiated a trial contract with the Ohio Bureau of Vocational Rehabilitation in an attempt to assure more effective collaboration and coordinated planning of social and vocational rehabilitation services.

Training

Hill House has at any given time two graduate social work students from Case Western Reserve University who are assigned to the agency for field work experience. These are concurrent placements during the entire academic year and have been filled since the program was initiated in 1964. It has not been able to provide for additional placements requested by the university; however, its projected program expansion includes a substantial increase in the training program.

The program participates in psychiatric nursing training programs of five local hospitals, and participates in the training of psychiatric residents from two state hospitals and one general hospital. Training is also provided during the summer months for undergraduate students.

Hill House recently accepted two additional graduate students for field work experience and has initiated a new program to train workers at the bachelor's level.

Finances

During its first five years the financial support for Hill House came entirely from two sources, a National Institute of Mental Health research-demonstration grant and local foundations. Starting in 1966 two additional sources of funds became available; Hill House was accepted by the Welfare Federation of Cleveland (United Appeal) as a funded agency, and a purchase-of-service contract was negotiated with the state of Ohio. The portions of funds during the past few years have been:

	1966	1967	1968	1969	1970
NIMH grant	33%	7%	0%	0%	0%
Local foundations	27	13	3	0	0
State of Ohio	24	50	40	61	65
Welfare Federation (United Appeal)	11	22	53	35	31
Fees and dues from members	0	1	1	1	1
Gifts and miscellaneous	5	7	3	3	3

The money received from the state government came initially through a purchase-of-service contract for aftercare. Under new mental health legislation that became effective in mid-1969, Hill House will be eligible for funding through the county mental health board on the basis of up to 75 percent from the state and at least 25 percent from the local community. Hill House anticipates that the bulk of its future income will be from this source.

Fees and dues from members were instituted only in 1967 and have not represented more than a tiny fraction of the income. Developed jointly by the board of trustees, members of the staff, and the professional advisory committee, the fee schedule runs from nothing to $15 per month, based on a formula which takes into account income, number of dependents, medical expenses, and other major debts or unusual expenses. An exception is the single, dependent member living with his parental family; fees are not charged "since we do not want to increase the dependence on the family, when our goal is employment and independence."

Fees are set in an interview between member and social worker

The agency's self-image and its future plans

There seemed to us to be an unsolved divergence of interests within the Hill House board and, to a lesser extent, within the staff with respect to comprehensive services. Hill House is doing precisely what it set out to do, and evidently succeeding in an orderly and structured way. There was never an intention that Hill House would expand into a large agency designed to meet all the socialization needs of all the persons being discharged to Cleveland.

In the latter respect the staff and the board seem to be entirely in agreement: if further capability and capacity for handling former mental hospital patients is needed in Cleveland, additional agencies should be established rather than to expand Hill House considerably, or even moderately, beyond its present size. Certain perceived advantages of relatively intimate and close-knit agencies are highly valued at Hill House, and one is hard put to disagree with the viewpoint.

It is more in the area of comprehensive program that the staff seem to see the need for expansion. To a considerable extent they seem to share the desire of their own members for a residential facility, particularly to provide a temporary haven to those undergoing particular stress.

The staff also express the belief that there are categories of potential members other than those who have been in state hospitals—people in the community with significant need for psychological support but in life circumstances that have enabled them to remain, marginally, in the community. Hill House recently received a grant to work with non-mental health agencies such as the YWCA and settlement houses to establish social groups intermixing this type of person with some of the Hill House members. Such groups might serve a dual purpose: to help to stabilize some of the Hill House members who seem ready to enter into social activities outside the agency's domain, and as a recruitment device for young people in the community who might benefit from the services of a psychosocial rehabilitation center.

SUMMARY AND PROSPECTS

XII. Some Viewpoints and Persuasions

THE SIX PROGRAMS THAT THE AUTHORS VISITED vary greatly from one to another in size of staff, size of client load, size of physical facility, centralized vs. deployed services, and relative emphasis within the program on vocational, residential, and social components.

There are important similarities, however, as well as a few differences in some other characteristics, and these were most evident at the time of our conference with the directors of the six programs we visited plus those from five other programs whom we also invited to participate. The viewpoints and persuasions of the eleven people who represented these programs come from many years of experience in dealing with some of the mental patients reputed to be the most difficult. Consequently, we will summarize their beliefs about how psychosocial rehabilitation programs ought to operate, what they ought to include, and what they ought to avoid.

We approached the conference by asking each delegate to play the role of a person charged with drawing up an ideal plan for the support and maintenance in the community of people impaired by serious mental illness, or from deficits left by or related to such an illness. In approaching the problem, we asked them to assume that all the money and all the manpower they needed would be available. Clearly, they found it difficult to do so, since most of them have been struggling from year to year to identify and recruit ample funds to stay in business. In some cases they have had to expand their programs not according to their own preferences but in the ways indicated by the available sources of funds.

Nonetheless, we found some important areas of agreement.

Clientele

All eleven programs are dealing for the most part with schizophrenics, and the considerable majority of these have undergone at least one spell of hospitalization in a state hospital, which is to be expected, since most of the programs were specifically established to try to provide some of the supports that the ex-state-hospital patient seemed to need. Most of them were established by people who were aware of and concerned about the large numbers of readmissions. Thus, schizophrenics constituted at least 65 percent of the clients in each of the programs. In recent years some of the programs have expressed a growing concern about the need to provide service to younger schizophrenics who, with the availability of treatment in community mental health centers and in general hospitals, are spared hospitalization in state hospitals; such people constituted about a quarter of the caseload in two of the agencies but a quite small minority in the others.

There was near unanimity about the need to screen out certain kinds of applicants. Most of the programs found alcoholics troublesome at best and impossible at worst, and some simply would not accept them. This refusal was voiced as a matter of the alcoholic's having too much ego strength to be integrated with the schizophrenic population, so that as a result the schizophrenic members would suffer. There was some concern that the alcoholic might come to the program drunk, thereby upsetting the other members and the staff and volunteers as well. For the most part, people with a variety of sexual problems were also screened out, particularly if there seemed any likelihood that their deviant urges would be acted upon. All of the programs did, however, intermix men and women, and there did not seem to have been any problems of sexual aggressiveness.

Prognostic skill

All eleven programs agreed that they seem to have very little capability to predict which applicants will do well and which will not after they have entered the program. There was considerable impatience with the diagnostic labels that the referring agents had attached to their members. Said one of the directors:

> Differentiation in diagnosis as for example between the various forms of schizophrenia does not turn out to be useful. There is little process information in diagnostic terms that we can use in dealing with a given individual. What our members have in common are these things: poor or disorganized ego structure or strength; poor skills, habits, and persistence regarding work performance in the community; poor social and family resources and relationships; poor social skills; a great amount of dependency; and such practical problems as the inability to have enough money, to find a suitable place to live without help, and to cope with a variety of day-by-day living problems.

The delegates were unanimous in declaring that standardized tests were not useful in predicting whether a person will do well or ill in the program. The predictive capability of existing tests is not considered good enough to justify taking up the time to administer and interpret them or exposing the patient to hours of testing. Furthermore, even if the tests were predictive, it would still be hard or impossible to translate a given set of scores into a specific program for a given individual. Some programs that used tests routinely in their earlier days have greatly curtailed them, and it seems safe to say that tests are used by and large only to meet the requirements of state rehabilitation agencies. Said one of the program directors:

> The use of standardized tests seems to be more for the person who is giving the test than for any value the tests have for the client.

Thus, evaluation is accomplished mainly through observation by staff, and to a limited extent by volunteers. Some of the programs have established definite observation periods, such as a month, and only after this time does the staff formulate a program for the particular client.

Refusals and dropouts

All eleven programs had many applicants who refused the service once it was explained to them, and another large number who, after entering the program, dropped out "unilaterally," that is, without the staff agreeing that they had obtained all the benefit that the program had to offer them. This is of course common in various types of mental health facilities; for example, the modal number of visits to practically all outpatient clinics is one. Typically, mental health facilities have not made much effort to reactivate the refusal or the dropout, largely because the existing demands for treatment take up all the available staff time; also, in many cases the dropout is presumed to be unmotivated, so that it would be pointless to invest the time in contacting him.

Three of the eleven psychosocial centers had made some effort to contact dropouts and refusals. Council House developed an interview form for dropouts and another for those who did not show up for their initial interview and found that "they weren't availing themselves of our service because of the illness."

> They were too regressed to come out; they didn't have the fortitude to come out. So they would say, If we had money, we'd come to the program. And we would reply, We'll give you carfare. They took the carfare and still did not come. Then they said, If somebody would go with us, we'd come. So we sent escorts, who literally had to dress some of the people. We didn't go much further, because by then we had decided that it's basically the illness.

Horizon House had attempted to reactivate dropouts by means of telephone contacts and home visits. They found that a single contact resulted in a reactivation of 38 percent, and, surprisingly, that the rate did not differ between the two methods of contact.

Time-limited vs. unlimited programs

The programs differed about whether a time-limited program was superior to an open-ended program in which the individual could maintain relationships indefinitely. Fountain House and Council House in particular are opposed to a time limit, because they are persuaded that many of the people they serve need support over a period of years and also because they have seen dramatic forward movement in individuals who have been stalemated for several years. Furthermore, as Council House put it, "Often there is nothing else available for our people except our program." Both of these programs do at the same time provide some time-limited vocational components for particular members who they think will be able to progress in a relatively short time. Thresholds takes a stand at the other extreme, on the grounds that the major determinant of a client's response will be the level of expectation. Said Mr. Dincin:

> Having no time limit vitiates the theory of expectations which we have found so valuable. If you don't expect things from your clients you generally don't get them.

But the time limit imposed by a number of the programs is honored more in the breach than in the observance. Only one program had ever terminated a member because she had exhausted the allotted time, and that because her lack of progress was felt to be the result of a destructive relationship with her parents, which she would not agree to modify. All of the time-limited programs had at least a few members who had been participating for more than the stipulated limit, which in every case was one year. (Hill House, which started with a six-month limit, soon found that "many of the changes we were looking for were not occurring in that period, since it took four months before a typical client had made any kind of beginning use of our service." Consequently the limit was increased to one year.)

This leads us to observe that there was no particular rationale that lay behind the one-year limit—nothing that emerged either from our interviews at these programs or from the review of the literature to indicate that this is an optimum or even a suitable span of time to allow for the stabilization or improvement of function in people many of whom have been socially dysfunctional for years, if not all their lives. Indeed, one could equally well argue that the client would find a second year useful during which to consolidate any gains of the first year. It appears that the one-year limit is simply one that seems compatible to the budgeting process and is not too threatening either to staff members whose morale requires some evidence of working with an upward-moving population or to funding agencies that are leery of committing themselves to programs of indefinite support to a limited number of people.

The solution pursued by Horizon House is to have a highly programmed time-limited sequence of one year, available to all those who can meet its demands, backed up by a second level of long-term supportive and maintenance service to those who cannot respond within a year.

Centralization vs. deployment

All eleven programs had started as centralized, "intown" programs, but with time several established satellites. In three cases this was attributable to affiliation agreements with community mental health centers under which staff could be made available to provide services within particular neighborhoods. There seemed to be full agreement that first a relatively strong central agency is needed, with deployment thereafter into local communities. An important reason for this is that many inner city people and blacks in particular are thought to avoid moving out of their own neighborhoods for services.

Whether to limit oneself to a single specialized agency that draws from an entire metropolitan area, or to branch out with a series of "satellite" services does not seem to be an all-or-none matter. Among the factors that must be considered are the convenience of the members and prospective members, availability of public transportation, the nature and expense of the particular program components, and increasing emphasis on vesting authority for services at the community level.

Staffing

There was unanimous agreement that personal characteristics of staff members are more important than their training. Said Mr. Lanoil of Fountain House:

> There has always been a tendency among agencies to get all the professional staff they can. But we are trying to create a new approach that maximizes the use of nonprofessionals and preprofessionals. This is not being done to save money, but rather because of the nature of what we're attempting to do; our population requires a diverse relatedness to various kinds of people. By providing varied kinds of staff, each

important in his own right, we can strengthen and enrich a program much more than when it is dominated by any particular discipline or combination of disciplines.

This is not to suggest that mental health professionals have no place in such programs; on the contrary, the same staff members who advocated extensive use of untrained staff agreed when pressed that their own professional training does help them in their work. But there was at the same time a feeling among the same professionals that very few mental health training programs provide much content about the maintenance and support of the long-term patient who has been discharged to the community. Consequently the professionals working in these programs felt that much of what they did that was useful consisted of things they had learned on the job, often through trial and error.

There is also the need to meet "legitimacy" and legal imperatives. That is, in many places the funding sources impose certain training minimums to qualify for financial support, and frequently referring agencies are loath to make referrals to programs that have few professionals on the staff. "Apart from these two considerations," said Dr. Rutman, "I would be hard put to maintain that professional training has been in and of itself a contribution to the quality of performance of a given individual. I can think of just as many cases on our staff where at least as good a job, sometimes a better one, was done by an untrained person."

Edward Spark of Montreal's Forward House sent a questionnaire to hospitals and other agencies asking their feelings about nonprofessionals working with the patients they refer. All of the respondents said they felt it was of no consequence, because of the good results they had seen from the program. About half of them added, however, that there should be adequate professional consultation available.

One might develop a paradigm for staff recruitment as follows: the most desirable staff member is the professional who has the appropriate personal characteristics, such as warmth, energy, and empathy, for working with this particular population; next would come the untrained person with the appropriate personal characteristics; third would come the trained person who lacks the desired personal characteristics; and last would come the untrained person without the appropriate personal characteristics. The first category is often difficult to find, and the second hardly less so. Consequently, in the face of a supply of mental health professionals that does not meet the demand, programs must sometimes settle for the third category. One would hope that there would be few from the fourth category, and that if they are unwittingly hired into a program their inappropriateness would soon be discovered and they would be steered to some other line of work.

The role of the psychiatrist ranged among these eleven programs from nonexistent to integral. Some had psychiatric treatment time regularly scheduled into the program, others had scheduled psychiatric consultation to the staff, others had psychiatric consultation available on call, and some had no psychiatric participation at all.

By and large psychiatrists were viewed as valuable, although almost exclusively because of their technical roles. They were considered useful for intervening in emergencies, consulting on physical or physiological matters, monitoring medication, and, when needed, prescribing medication. The programs agreed, however, that there did not seem to be anything specific to the training of psychiatrists that gave them particular competence in the programs of psychosocial centers (they felt the same about all of the other disciplines, too, including rehabilitation counseling). "If the psychiatrist feels he should play a role in programs of our kind," said Mr. Dincin, "the first thing he should do is get some training in rehabilitation."

One program reported that it had made considerable efforts to involve psychiatric residents in its activities in order that they might have some exposure to community-based rehabilitation efforts, but it had little success.

> We could never get more than one resident at a time to come. He would get his back to the wall and involve himself in such a way that he wouldn't have to move around, and then he'd leave early. I think this results from the nature of their training, with so much emphasis on one-to-one psychotherapy.

Council House was the only program using nurses. Its director, Lois Evey, has a master's degree in nursing education. She has had four nurses on the staff over the years, and she recommends them.

> We see nurses as being rather unprejudiced and quite flexible. Typically they have been the closest to patients. I can assign nurses on my staff to just about anything, and they don't back off. They'll say, I'm sure I can do it, or at least I'll try.

Fountain House had successfully hired eight of its members into regular full-time staff jobs, for the most part clerical.

We felt, after having talked to so many of the staff members, that they seemed uncommonly invested in what they were doing. The hours of operation and the type of interactions between staff and members were such as to suggest a client-focused philosophy exceeding what we have seen in most mental health facilities. We also felt that if we were assigned the job of recruiting a staff for a psychosocial center we would seek people discontented with the traditions of their disciplines. Morale was extremely high among the staffs of the six centers we visited, and we believed it was partly because they had kicked over the traces of traditional services in favor of something with more compatible goals and modes of operation. This characteristic was most poignantly expressed by Mrs. Evey.

> I left the state system because I couldn't stand to see a patient that we sent home with her hair all done and wearing a new dress come back to us two or three weeks later, incoherent and unable to recognize us. I started wondering, What demon out there is doing this? I had to go and find out.

Volunteers

Although most of the eleven programs used volunteers, there were conflicting opinions about the desirability of having them and the extent of their usefulness; comments ranged from highly enthusiastic to moderately negative. The two largest and longest-established centers, Fountain House and Horizon House, give the least emphasis to volunteers. Mr. Lanoil said that

> Fountain House de-emphasized the volunteer function, because it seemed to interfere with our emphasis on having the members themselves take on ever greater responsibility.

The few volunteers used at Fountain House are involved only because they have specific skills that are useful in leading particular activity programs.

Thresholds indicates that its emphasis on volunteers has diminished over the years, but it nonetheless has 45 presently participating. Ten of these are students from the University of Chicago who run the Saturday program without any staff participation.

Boston's Center Club uses 35 students from surrounding colleges, mostly recruited through psychology and sociology departments. Forward House in Montreal has 35 teenagers who come weekly to participate with members in dancing, playing games, singing around the piano, and just talking. Portals not only has about 25 active volunteers but also a staff position for volunteer coordinator.

The rationale for using volunteers is not that they augment or save staff time. Said Mrs. Sue Messitte of the Albert Deutsch Center in Washington, D.C.:

We have used volunteers from the outset, but not because they help to relieve the staff or to save staff time. To the contrary, they require a considerable investment of staff time. But we use them because we feel they're a very necessary link to the community.

Only two of the programs will allow former members to become volunteers.

Involvement of families

There has been a rising interest in the past few years in involving families of patients in the treatment process. Dr. H. G. Whittington calls family therapy "the only really new treatment approach of the 1960's." However, a 1969 study* of staff members in eight community mental health centers showed that less than two percent of staff time was being spent in family therapy. Several of the psychosocial centers were unenthusiastic about the potential for involving families in a helpful way. Said Council House:

> We believe that our program is a laboratory for training where one can learn new skills and make changes in behavior, possibly by making mistakes but still having the support of others around you. This is why we keep families out, so that our members won't have to make mistakes in front of the same parents who have been giving them a hard time.

Mr. Dincin said that Thresholds has attempted to involve families in special orientation sessions, and that this has occasionally proved helpful in the case of younger members; however,

> when we are dealing with a thirty- or forty-year-old unemancipated person, we find that the rigidity of the parental family is such as to make intervention impossible.

Thresholds had, however, involved spouses and children of members in a summer camping program with good results.

> This proved to be a rewarding experience both from our own diagnostic understanding and also from the member's point of view.

The Albert Deutsch Center of Washington had found it useful to involve parents and sometimes spouses.

> Once we establish a good relationship with the client, and provided the family understands that we are "an agency of last resort," we find their involvement to be a considerable help.

---

*R. M. Glasscote and J. E. Gudeman: *The Staff of the Mental Health Center: A Field Study.* Joint Information Service, Washington, D.C., 1969.

In summary, the eleven programs appeared to feel that *a*) they should be making greater efforts to involve families, but *b*) their experiences to date have frequently not been successful, with the family often attempting to hold the client down or refusing to cooperate in his emancipation. The programs did not seem to be doing anything either systematic or very original with families; at most they seemed to be letting relatives come in occasionally to selected program activities. The role of the family has been limited in most cases because the agency is inclined to think it is a losing effort or is in some way inappropriate. Dr. Rutman suggested that

> perhaps it's really because we haven't felt we had the time or the staff or the energy to get into still another thrust, so that we have taken the easy way out. I submit that we don't yet know. We haven't made a good beginning toward learning what the effective use of families might be.

Sources of funds

All of the centers were largely dependent on public funds from one or several sources, including staffing grants from the federal community mental health center program, grants-in-aid from state mental health departments, and purchase-of-service arrangements with the state rehabilitation agencies. Several received a portion, albeit a fairly limited one, of their budget from the local community fund. Few received more than a tiny fraction of funds from fees or dues paid by members, in some cases because there was a policy against charging for service, but more often simply because most of the members are poor people.

What we have in these agencies is a modern American paradox—a group of private nonprofit programs very largely dependent upon public funding for their continued existence. There was a consensus among them that this was an appropriate mode of funding such services—that the private agency possessed an efficiency and innovativeness that public agencies oftentimes do not have. Among these eleven programs, only Fountain House obtained more than half of its budget from private sources.

Inevitably much of the discussion about financing centered upon the state rehabilitation agency. Most of the programs were receiving some or a good deal of their operating funds from this source. Five of the eleven indicated that they felt their experience with their state rehabilitation agencies was generally satisfactory. Three others felt that it was unsatisfactory, and another three that it was grossly unsatisfactory. Said one of the dissatisfied program directors:

> The rehabilitation program has its origins in services to the physically disabled and they have not managed to adapt their viewpoint sufficiently to the particular needs of the mentally ill.

Another program director agreed, adding that the rehabilitation agency in his state was "too much centered on the sheltered workshop," and another added that the rehabilitation agency had tended to use her program as "a dumping ground."

There was much criticism of the practice in many states of counting a case as successfully rehabilitated after the client had been on the job for thirty days. This period was felt to be much too brief for the mentally ill. The delegates agreed that the length of employment for successful closure for mental patients ought to be at least six months and perhaps as long as a year.

This leads us to observe that the point of contact with the state rehabilitation agency is typically with a rehabilitation counselor. The training of most rehabilitation counselors does not seem to include very much content about mental illness, a situation that led several of the program directors to complain that the rehabilitation agency seems to have little understanding of what *social* rehabilitation attempts to do and the longer-term educative process that it entails.

Said one program director:

> We are almost forced into an adversary relationship with the local rehabilitation agency, in which we're wheedling and negotiating constantly so that we can get the initial acceptances and the subsequent extensions that our clients need.

Under the provisions of the federal-state rehabilitation program, funds are available only on a purchase-of-service basis. Eight of the eleven programs represented at the conference said they would prefer a block grant for "program support" rather than payment on the existing basis of contracted services.

We have earlier described how the federal regulations will allow states to provide support for mental illness clients for as long as eighteen months. However, none of the eight states in which these facilities are located had elected to do so. The most favorable arrangement was the one prevailing in New Jersey, where 46 weeks of regular sponsorship are provided. In other cases, "Personal Adjustment Training" and prevocational training programs contracted by the state agency typically last for thirteen weeks or twenty weeks, with extensions sometimes available. However, the program directors clearly felt that, for example, a thirteen-week program followed by a thirteen-week extension was not an adequate period of time for re-educating people who had been poorly adjusted socially for a great many years, if not all of their lives.

Rehabilitation process and philosophy

These programs tend to see their contribution as in three parts: *a*) a laboratory for socialization in which the sanctions are not as great as in the community at large; *b*) a down-to-earth advocacy role; and *c*) a supportive relationship much more informal than the typical psycho-therapeutic relationship. All of them do conceive of what they do as "therapeutic," although some of them seem to be reticent about admitting to this because of their concern that, since they are not under ultimate medical direction, they might incur the wrath of the medical agencies that they must deal with.

There was a conviction that rehabilitation centers ought not to be located in hospitals. Said Mrs. Evey:

> If the center is attached to a hospital, then the client must go back into the hospital, which he will probably resent. We have found that we can't even schedule a social event in the hospital, even though the hospitals have offered their facilities to us free of charge. By contrast, the client can come to us in the community without having to be threatened about being readmitted to the hospital. He can talk to us about a problem without being afraid that we will say, "Aha, you'd better get to your doctor."

But she adds that she thinks a community mental health center could accomplish these rehabilitation functions perfectly well as long as they were not carried out in a hospital building.

Dr. Rutman sees the relationship between staff and member as different in important respects from the traditional helping person-client relationship.

> It comes somewhere close to, but doesn't actually reach, a peer relationship. We are viewing our members not as people we are helping, but rather as people with whom we are interacting.

There was an acknowledgement, however, that despite their social and educative focus the programs have by and large incorporated psychiatric theory. Although the theory may be adapted to meet the particular needs of the rehabilitation program, nonetheless, as one director expressed it:

> It is helpful to know that there are some kinds of things that cause anxiety and other kinds of things that relieve it; that there are kinds of things that put people in a bind, and others that avoid it.

The authors felt that, to the extent clinicians are still taught an "objective" stance with patients, that is, to avoid becoming personally involved, this approach would not seem to work in the psychosocial centers. It appeared to us that the programs were posited on the assumption that it was necessary to become deeply involved in the member's life in the community. In this respect they seem to be at the other end of the spectrum from classical psychotherapy.

XIII. An Eye to the Future

W HEN WE CONTRAST the present state of development of rehabilitation resources and the numbers of people they serve with the situation as it was thirty years ago, we can find much to be enthusiastic about. In 1940 there were only the beginnings of a conviction that many of the people who have been or still are mentally ill could be trained and supported in ways that would enable them to live in the community, in many cases working enough to earn their own way. We have briefly described some of the major developments and advances in treating, training, and supporting capability that have come into being during that time. We have observed how dramatically the state hospital population has been reduced, how the length of treatment in community-based treatment services has progressively shortened, and how such transitional and supporting resources as halfway houses, workshops, and ex-patient clubs have increased in number. We have indicated the intertwining with these developments of such enhanced sources of support as the broadened federal rehabilitation program, the emergence of the federal community mental health center program, and the growth in mental illness benefits in voluntary health insurance.

All of this progress is best viewed, nonetheless, as an encouraging beginning. There are perhaps 3000 persons with a history of mental illness living in halfway houses, and at most a few thousand working in sheltered workshops. Despite the rapid increase in rehabilitation closures under the aegis of the state rehabilitation agencies, the number (excluding alcoholics and neurotics) had reached only about 34,000 by 1969. There is still a long way to go before services are developed and organized to the extent that every person undergoing hospitalization for mental illness will be adequately evaluated to determine whether he needs any or all of the rehabilitative services to help him to live as autonomously and meaningfully as his particular individual condition will allow.

Research

A research effort greatly exceeding what has taken place to date seems to be needed in many aspects of rehabilitating the mentally ill.

We heard again and again in our interviews that the rehabilitation centers had no predictive capability. Clients who seemed highly promising in terms of test scores, general intelligence, affect, insight, and motivation often failed miserably; others who had been hospitalized for many years and seemed to have very little to rehabilitate often did well. It is truly tempting, in these circumstances, simply to declare that "the human equation" will always be insuperable, that research efforts are therefore useless, and that rehabilitation programs should simply be planned to give a trial-and-error opportunity to as many comers as the available staff, money, and physical plants will allow.

For the time being, that probably is in fact the best that can be done. In terms of long-range planning, it seems too pessimistic, expensive, and wasteful.

What one would hope for from more intensive and extensive research efforts would be data that would allow one, first of all, to predict the rehabilitation potential, so that he could with some justification divide prospects according to level of potentiality. Beyond this, one would hope for evaluative techniques that would enable him to differentiate particular programs for candidates with particular characteristics and aptitudes. Such research can probably be done in some existing rehabilitation services, provided it is designed to include a respectable number of experimental and control subjects and is funded over a reasonable period of time, for example, five years or longer.

An interesting approach, we feel, would be a large-scale community-wide study involving a series of community mental health centers and an adequate network of rehabilitation resources. As of now there do not seem to be any communities where this would be possible, since none are completely covered by operating mental health centers plus an ample supply of halfway houses, workshops, and psychosocial centers. (Philadelphia and Pittsburgh are two cities that promise in time to reach this stage of development.)

Training

We heard throughout this study that mental health professionals typically receive little training—sometimes none at all—in the rehabilitation process. Staff members of the psychosocial centers, many of whom are themselves mental health professionals, deplored the tendency of people working in treating facilities to view their job as ended when the patient's acute disturbance is brought under control. It appears that training programs do not adequately emphasize that some of the more troubling forms of mental illness are frequently relapsing, often leave deficits, and require a long-term and continuous commitment.

On the other hand, we often heard the complaint that rehabilitation personnel do not know enough about the characteristics of mental illness and the long-term process involved in social rehabilitation of mentally ill people. It appears that most rehabilitation curricula, while they focus heavily on courses in psychology, do not have much specific content about mental illness, and most of them do not have a practicum.* Thus, it seems desirable that mental health training programs affiliate with rehabilitation resources in order to provide some first-hand exposure to the rehabilitation process. Rehabilitation training programs might benefit by affiliation with mental health facilities whereby the trainees could become educated to the characteristics of mental illness.

Services

There seems a need for improvement both in the amount and the characteristics of the rehabilitation services that are presently available. While many communities now have Goodwill Industries and Jewish Vocational Service workshops, many others do not. While about ninety communities have halfway houses serving the mentally ill, there are many others that have no provision at all for transitional residence. In the whole country there are only a few of the comprehensive rehabilitation centers of the kind described in previous chapters of this report. The proliferation of rehabilitation resources in recent years has been impressive, but many more are needed.

By and large, the services of these various resources to their clients need to be longer term. We believe that the time limits typically set by the psychosocial centers and halfway houses are related not to any concrete knowledge of how long it takes a mental illness client to become capable of autonomous living, but rather to considerations of budgeting and staff morale. There may need to be both high-expectation programs and low-expectation programs. Ideally the applicant might first be given an opportunity in the high-expectation setting, and, if he cannot succeed there, be given a subsequent opportunity in the low-expectation setting. Perhaps only if he fails there should one consider whether he will be best served by the protection of a hospital.

---

*Important exceptions are three training centers for rehabilitation counselors, at the Massachusetts Mental Health Center, Nebraska Psychiatric Institute, and the University of Oregon; by 1970 these three centers, especially developed in the early 1960's to train rehabilitation counselors to deal with mental illness clients, had graduated more than 200 counselors.

In all aspects of rehabilitation services—if not within mental health centers as well—there should be more emphasis on recruiting jobs for mental illness clients. There does not seem to be any magic about getting employers to take a chance with people who have a history of mental illness. Many will not, of course, but there is abundant evidence that some will; consider particularly the experience of Fountain House, which has placed hundreds of its members in jobs. Especially promising are industries and businesses that have a high turnover of personnel and where many of the jobs demand only limited skills. (It seems evident that many persons with a history of long-term mental illness can tolerate half-time jobs, but not full-time jobs, for which reason it may be necessary to arrange with the prospective employer to split a full-time job between two persons.) From what we heard from certain of the centers described herein, it is perfectly possible, with initiative and persistence, to recruit the jobs for clients that they may not be able to locate for themselves. Some employers seem particularly responsive when, as in the case of Fountain House, the rehabilitation facility promises to back up the client by sending a substitute in case he is unable to come to work himself.

Auspices and locus

We have attempted to give appropriate credit to the state hospitals for the progress they have made in mounting rehabilitation services. About one out of ten has a comprehensive rehabilitation program. This is desirable and in the patient's interest. However, it does not seem sufficient. Particularly as the period of stay for new admissions grows shorter and shorter, there is a reduced opportunity to expose the patient to the long-term re-educative experiences that are called for in rehabilitation. Thus, however successful a start is provided within the state hospital, many patients are likely to need continued opportunities in a community-based program. Furthermore, if our national purpose is to make it possible for the mentally ill to be treated in the community and to live in the community, then it makes sense for the rehabilitation effort to be there as well.

WE DID NOT UNDERTAKE this study of psychosocial rehabilitation centers under the persuasion that there should be a great many such programs developed around the country. We did not have enough evidence to be persuaded one way or the other. Rather, we chose them for their comprehensiveness, thinking that their experiences would promise useful information for planning further rehabilitation programs. Even after having visited them, interviewed their clients, and met in conference with them, it is still not possible for us to recommend that such facilities should be replicated throughout the United States. Certainly, one must acknowledge that some of these programs are extremely attractive in terms of philosophy, goals, program, and staff. There are some important tentative indications that the comprehensive autonomous center is a viable approach to providing rehabilitation services. At the same time, out of the growing interest in reducing the historic fragmentation of mental health services might come the conclusion that it would be better for each community mental health center to acquire, either within its own framework or by a truly effective liaison arrangement with other resources, its own access to rehabilitation services for its clients. In this regard, however, it seems important to keep in mind that much of the special quality and flavor of these centers stems from the fact that they are physically located outside treating facilities.

The Horizon House and Council House programs should be of particular interest for the very reason that they are arranging to serve as the rehabilitation arm of some of the mental health centers serving certain catchment areas of their respective communities.

Five Brief Program Descriptions

*This appendix consists of brief descriptions of five psychosocial reha-
bilitation centers that were not included in the field study but whose
directors attended the conference previously described. The material
that follows is based on the reports of programs that the directors themselves presented at this conference. The descriptions have not been up-
dated and should therefore be understood to reflect the content and
nature of these programs as they existed at the end of 1969.*

Forward House, Montreal

Forward House was started in 1957 by six people who had been
patients in a Montreal mental hospital, who initially met once a week
at a downtown YMCA. By the time the membership had reached 25,
the group asked a local service organization to provide them some
money to employ part-time staff that would help them to locate jobs
and a better quality of housing, and provide opportunities for socialization. The organization did so, in 1959, and the membership grew to about
125, with programs taking place four evenings each week. Psychiatric
residents from the local hospital served as part-time group workers, and
there was a part-time executive director. The program continued to expand, and in 1964 moved into a duplex building. The membership during 1969 was 400, with at least 200 active during any given month. The
1970 budget was $53,000, of which about two thirds came from the
government of the Province of Quebec, another $10,000 from the spon-
soring service club. The staff has grown to a full-time executive director,
a full-time program director, three full-time employment rehabilitation
workers, and seven psychiatric residents serving part time as group
workers. The program has decentralized to some extent; a young adults
group takes place at the YMCA, and another community group meets
in a settlement house.

Center Club, Boston

The Center Club originated in 1959 with group meetings of ex-mental
patients at the Massachusetts Association for Mental Health; later, the
meetings were held in a church which donated space. The initial staff

consisted of one professional and one volunteer. Within a year, membership had grown from eight to about 120, and the club moved into larger quarters in a downtown YMCA. In 1963, a three-year vocational rehabilitation grant, subsequently extended for a year, was awarded to study prevocational planning and work conditioning for seriously handicapped mental patients. During 1969 there were 418 persons who took some part in the program. The club is open 75 hours a week, from 9:15 a.m. to 10:00 p.m. Mondays through Fridays, from 10:00 a.m. to 5:00 p.m. on Saturdays, and from 1:00 to 6:00 p.m. on Sundays. The program includes social, recreational, educational, and cultural activities, and in the recent past has increasingly emphasized a daytime prevocational program, including a small workshop that has several subcontracts. There is a great deal of crisis counseling, personal adjustment counseling, job counseling, group therapy, and an information and referral service. The club has affiliated with the Tufts University Mental Health Center, in whose catchment area it is located, and has been moving in the direction of developing "drop-in" satellites; one was opened in 1969 and another was scheduled to open in 1970. The club is in process of purchasing a halfway house in its South Boston area, with accommodations for 25 to 30 ex-patients. The staff consists of seven full-time and five part-time people. There are 35 student volunteers per semester, plus three from work-study programs and five from the Massachusetts Service Corps. The 1970 budget was $100,000, with anticipation of an expansion, particularly related to acquisition of the halfway house, to about $150,000. The quarters are in space rented from the YMCA.

Albert Deutsch Center, Washington, D.C.

The Albert Deutsch Center was started in 1966 by the District of Columbia Mental Health Association. The initial funds were raised by two large benefits given by the Association prior to the Center's opening. The District of Columbia Department of Vocational Rehabilitation assigned a staff member to operate the program on a half-time basis. This arrangement continued until 1968, when the Center incorporated and established its own board of directors. It then opened on a full-time basis with a professional staff of two; the DVR-assigned director became the full-time director, and a program coordinator was added. Located in a four-story town house, the Center serves about 200 patients a year, of which about 130 remain actively in the program. The program is divided into two parts; one is prevocational, the other is for people who are probably not going to be able to obtain remunerative employment.

The emphasis is on a group approach, with a minimum of individual counseling. In the afternoons there is a large recreational and cultural program run primarily by volunteers. Some of the members themselves do volunteer work in the city. The staff still consists of two full-time professionals, augmented by a large corps of volunteers, students, and mental health aides assigned from the health department. The 1970 budget was $71,000, provided principally by a contract with the Department of Vocational Rehabilitation, and supplemented by donations and Medicaid payments. A fee-for-service system was planned to start in 1970 for those members not eligible for Medicaid.

Stairways, Erie, Pennsylvania

Stairways originated in 1961 as a volunteer agency under United Fund and continued operating as such with a staff of two until 1967, when it became an agency of the Erie County Mental Health-Mental Retardation program. Stairways has affiliation agreements with two community mental health centers in Erie County, and its members are referred from these centers as well as from a state hospital and from privately practicing psychiatrists. About sixty members take part in the program each week. Stairways is open six days a week and has evening hours twice a week. The program includes professional counseling, social and recreational activities, and a telephone answering service for working with members and their families in crises. Stairways averages about 140 interviews a month with members and relatives. Vocational training is carried out through liaison with other local agencies; Stairways also has a "member worker" program, employing six or seven members in maintenance work at the house for which they are paid. A small transitional residential program was planned to start in 1970. In 1969 Stairways moved into a new location, a large old mansion which houses its offices and activities center. In addition, a sixteen-unit building has been leased for the residential program. Students and houseparents will be housed there, along with the residents. The staff as of the end of 1969 consisted of the director, a caseworker, a business manager, two secretaries, students from work-study programs, houseparents, and volunteers. The 1970 budget was $100,000, compared with $18,000 only two years ago. All the funds come from the Erie County Mental Health-Mental Retardation program.

Friendship House, Hackensack, New Jersey

Friendship House was started in 1956 by a women's volunteer group, as a service for individuals who were being discharged from the state hospital. It continued as a volunteer service project until 1962, when Fountain House of New York assigned one of its professional staff to Friendship House. An average of 65 persons per week are served. The members are generally young adults; there have never been any age limits, but most are in the 25-to-30 age group. The program is open six days a week and one evening. The emphasis is on vocational training on Mondays through Fridays, while on Thursday evenings and Saturdays the program is primarily social. Friendship House has a sheltered workshop which is being expanded to include a fairly wide variety of assembling and packing tasks as well as technical work assignments. Members are involved with the maintenance of the house — cleaning, cooking, driving, and so on. Job counseling is also provided. An accredited special education program for fourteen- to eighteen-year-olds operates five days a week. Pupils are referred from the local public schools, which reimburse Friendship House. The program was originally housed in a storefront, but it has moved twice and is now located in a new building funded by a construction grant from the Social and Rehabilitation Service. The professional staff consists of six full-time and two part-time persons. Two years ago Friendship House became part of a community mental health center, and it is also affiliated with Hackensack Hospital. It operates on an annual budget of $100,000, with funds coming from the state rehabilitation agency, fund-raising functions, and community support. In the future Friendship House hopes to open a transitional residence for fifteen to twenty people.

APPENDIX II

Questionnaire to Psychosocial Rehabilitation Centers

1. In what year did your program begin operation?_____

2. Under what auspices/sponsorship/ownership does the program operate?

3. On what days of the week and during what hours are you open?

4. What are the principal sources from which clients are referred to you?

5. Do you give preference to any particular categories of clients? (If "yes," specify).

6. Do you exclude any particular categories of clients? (If "yes," specify).

7. How many clients participate in your program in a typical week?_____

8. What is the approximate size of your budget for the current year?_____

9. What are the two or three principal sources of funds?

10. If you are in any way at all related to or affiliated with a community mental health center, please describe the relationship or affiliation.

11. Please list the staff currently working in the program.

Job title	Highest degree	No. of hours worked per week

Orientation Questionnaire to Psychosocial Rehabilitation Centers

1. Briefly describe how the program came to be organized, what agencies and individuals played a role in this organization, and when. What organizational steps were taken within the community? What leadership or political support was enlisted, if any?

2. Describe the legal base or charter, the governing body, and the interrelationship between this body and the staff.

3. Describe your system of fees, indicating how it was developed, any revisions that have been made and why, and how it is applied at present.

4. Please provide a breakdown of the principal sources of funds for your current budget (dollar amounts), from client fees, county, state, federal, donations, etc.

5. What are your prospects for future funds, both the stability of the old sources and the likelihood of new?

6. For all new clients or members who came into the program during any recent 12-month period for which you have data available, please indicate the numbers in the major diagnostic categories.

7. For the clients or members served during any recent 12-month period for which you have data available, please indicate the age and sex distribution according to the following intervals:

	No. men	No. women
Under 21		
21-30		
31-40		
41-50		
51-60		
61+		

8. Please estimate the percent of your clients or members who fall in the following categories:

	Men	*Women*
Living with parents	———	———
Living with spouses and/or children	———	———
Living with others than above	———	———
Living alone	———	———

9. Of those clients who have participated in your program in any recent 12-month period for which you have data available, how many were:

	Men	*Single women*	*Married women*
Competitively employed full time	———	———	———
Competitively employed part time	———	———	———
Employed in sheltered setting full time	———	———	———
Employed in sheltered setting part time	———	———	———
Unemployed	———	———	———
Not in the labor market	———	———	———

10. What categories of persons are excluded from your program, and, for each category, why?

11. What categories are preferred?

12. For applicants considered not appropriate to or eligible for your program, what kind of referral efforts do you make?

13. Are there any categories of patients or potential sources of clients not now coming to you that you feel you could serve successfully?

14. Do you allow a person who has "dropped out" or has been "separated," "terminated," or "discharged" from the program to return at a later time? If so, is he counted again?

15. If you have written rules, *please furnish a copy*. Also, indicate how the rules are developed, how they are revised, how enforced, and what the penalties are for infractions.

16. How are program revisions made? What components have been eliminated from the program and why? What are you planning to add?

17. For any recent 12-month period for which you have data available, please indicate the sources from which clients were referred to you.

	Number
Self-referred	_____
Family or friend	_____
Member or client	_____
Psychiatrist in private practice	_____
State hospital	_____
Community mental health center	_____
General hospital	_____
State vocational rehabilitation agency	_____
Other sources (specify)	_____

18. Describe any contractual or otherwise formalized arrangements for services you provide to or receive from other agencies.

19. In contrast with the formalized arrangements described above, indicate your most important informal relationships with other agencies.

20. Describe your intake procedure, including (a) the criteria by which it is decided whether or not a person should be accepted as a client; (b) the way in which he is evaluated; (c) the means by which a program is formulated for him. If a program is formulated, who participates in developing it? Does the client have anything to say about it?

21. Describe any requirements of the program for the client to have a physician, psychiatrist, or other therapeutic backup.

22. Do you place any limit on the length of time a client may participate in your program? If "yes," please explain the rationale. Has the program developed any persuasion about *optimal* length of participation for various categories of clients?

23. Describe the extent to which you involve the family of the client in the program.

24. If home visits to clients or members are ever made, describe the reasons and the procedure.

25. Are any of the elements of the program compulsory for the clients? Is there any required minimum extent of participation? Is there any limit imposed on the extent of participation?

26. Do you provide anything within your program itself that you consider to be treatment or therapy? If "yes," please describe.

27. What placements that you feel you need for your clients are presently unavailable to you?

28. How do your clients obtain medication?

29. Are there member/client officers, a house committee, a "member government" arrangement, etc.?

30. Describe fully your activities relating to work, including vocational assessment, vocational training either within your own program or by an informal or formal arrangement with other agencies, recruitment of jobs, placement of clients in jobs, follow-up of clients placed in jobs, etc.

31. Do you in any way follow up clients or members who are absentees from scheduled activities or who "drop out"? If "yes," describe.

32. What efforts have you made to obtain "outcome data" that would indicate the "success" of the program? What criteria were used to determine successful outcome?

33. Describe any research you may have done in addition to efforts to obtain outcome data.

34. What are the program's goals for the future? In what directions would you like to expand or augment the program?

35. What aspect(s) of the program are you least satisfied with at the present time?

36. Describe any satellite programs that are operated by your facility.

37. Has the program given any thought to the possibility or suitability of expanding the program to serve other than the psychiatric population?

38. Describe the use of volunteers, including the means by which they are recruited, the extent of orientation or training, the means of supervising their activities, the amount of time they devote, and the things they do.

39. Describe any training of students that goes on within your program. If there is none, have you explored the possibilities, and are you interested in developing such training?

40. Was there any opposition from the neighborhood, any special group, or any other source to the establishment of your program?

41. To what extent does the community appear to have knowledge of the existence and purpose of your program? To what extent do you feel you have community support and participation?

42. What state, county, and municipal regulations about licensure, occupancy, etc., apply to your program?

43. What legal responsibilities and/or obligations does your program have to and for the members or clients?

44. Have any lawsuits been brought against you? Have you been involved in any legal proceedings? (If "yes," describe).

45. What insurance do you carry other than property?